573

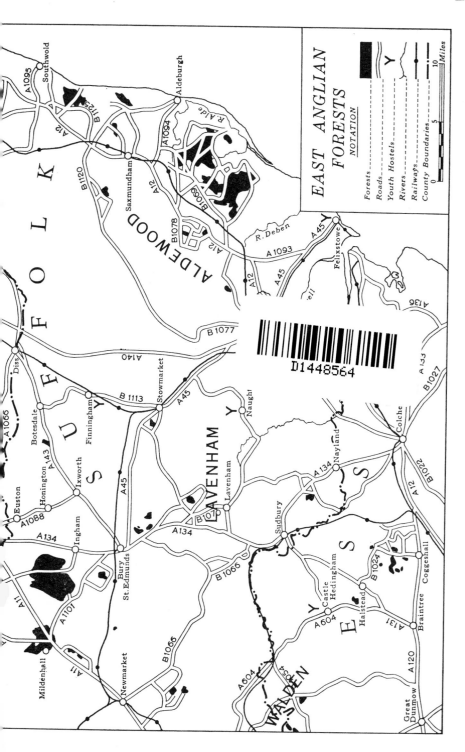

EAST ANGLIAN
FORESTS
NOTATION

Forests
Roads
Youth Hostels
Rivers
Railways
County Boundaries

0   5   10
Miles

D1448564

EAST ANGLIAN FORESTS GUIDE

Cover picture: Autumn sunlight in Thetford Forest. Scots pines (left), Corsican pines, beech, bracken, riders and roe deer

Back cover: Picnic place beside beeches and Corsican pine, on the road from Brandon to Bury St. Edmunds

Red deer stag drinking

FORESTRY COMMISSION GUIDE

EAST ANGLIAN
FORESTS

Edited by
HERBERT L. EDLIN, B.Sc., Dip.For.
Forestry Commission

LONDON
HER MAJESTY'S STATIONERY OFFICE
1972

CONTENTS

Beech

V

ACKNOWLEDGMENTS

Cover Picture by Charles Tunnicliffe, R.A.

Colour Photo on back cover by Herbert L. Edlin.

The Frontispiece is by Edmund Czarnowski, and the *Title page decoration* by George Mackley. *Line Drawings* throughout the text are by Noel Spencer, A.R.C.A., of Norwich Art School, except for the plant studies and the crossbill, which are by Ruth M. Race.

Aerial Photos. The air views to illustrate the articles on 'Topography, Geology and Soils' and 'Antiquities and History' are by Dr. J. K. St. Joseph. They are drawn from the collection of the Cambridge University Committee on Aerial Photography and are reproduced by kind permission of that Committee. Mr. I. A. Anderson, the Forestry Commission's Principal Photographer, took the view over Thetford Forest pine plantations.

Photos of Beasts and Birds. Most of these have been supplied by John Markham, a leading natural history photographer, who made special excursions to the Dunwich plantations in Aldewood Forest, Suffolk. Geoffrey Kinns photographed the otter.

Forest Views, etc. The majority of these are drawn from the Forestry Commission's collection, as shown by reference numbers. They are the work of Mr. I. A. Anderson and his skilled staff. In addition, thanks are due to the following photographers for their respective contributions: Mrs. G. M. McKay for Plates 10 and 21; the Castle Museum, Norwich for Plate 59; the magazine *Illustrated* for Plate 22, and the *Commercial Motor* for Plates 48, 49 and 50.

Barbara Green, Keeper of Archaeology at the Castle Museum, Norwich, kindly read through the article on Antiquities and History.

SBN 11   710032   3

Sweet chestnut

The Peddars Way, near Shadwell

INTRODUCTION

BY HERBERT L. EDLIN

EAST ANGLIA, England's richest agricultural province, holds some surprisingly large expanses of infertile sandy heaths that have proved unrewarding to the farmer. The most remarkable tract is that called the Breckland, around Thetford and Brandon on the borders of Norfolk and Suffolk. This region of sterile, dry, drifting sands held so little promise of successful cultivation that it became available, during the 1920's, to the newly-formed Forestry Commission for a great new enterprise of afforestation. Now fifty years later, the flourishing Thetford Forest of Scots and Corsican pines covers eighty square miles of the former barren heaths, yielding a sustained annual harvest of timber for industry.

As the pinewoods approach maturity, they are acquiring a new value as places for recreation and nature study. In contrast to the intensively cropped land around them, they offer opportunities for rambling, riding, camping, and roadside picnics. They are places

1

where people can halt awhile for a rest in the peace of the country-side, or explore cool shaded vistas running far beneath the spreading trees, sheltered alike from keen winds or glaring sun.

Following its policy of encouraging public recreation, the Forestry Commission is developing halting places and walks at several well-chosen points in Thetford Forest. This Guide has been planned to let people know where to find them, and also to show how much of scientific and historical interest an inquiring visitor can discover on his explorations. Leading authorities on geology and soils, plant and animal life, and the region's human history, have therefore been asked to outline the fascinating features that distinguish East Anglia from the rest of Britain. The forest staff complete the story, relating how the woods were created on the inhospitable bare land, and how they are sustained in their beauty today, whilst still proving profitable, employing labour, and yielding timber.

The smaller, outlying forests of this region—Aldewood near Woodbridge, Wensum north of Norwich, and Lynn close to the town of King's Lynn, are equally attractive. All stand near East Anglia's varied coastline of cliff, shingle bank and estuary, and close to wide broads or deep slow-flowing rivers. The car parks, picnic places, and walks that are being opened at each major woodland enable people to enjoy a marked variety of scenery in the agricultural, marshland, or seashore landscapes around them. Each of the fifty woodlands concerned was first chosen for planting because its soil was poor, or the former woodland had been cleared, but by a happy chance they lie amid the very finest scenery that East Anglia can offer, and are usually remote from holiday crowds. The maps and directions herein will help you to find these charming spots.

The artist who made our text drawings, Noel Spencer of Norwich, has visited many of these outlying woods with a keen eye for their individual character. His sensitive interpretation of Norfolk and Suffolk scenes show just what the appreciative visitor should seek. Follow the paths he took, as I have done, and you will be richly rewarded.

The visitor's interest in the topography of East Anglia will like-wise extend beyond the forest boundaries. Dr. R. M. S. Perrin, of the Cambridge University Department of Applied Biology, reviews both the underlying geological structure and the surface soils of the whole region, illustrating his points with maps. The University's Committee on Aerial Photography has supplemented this by a splendid group of aerial photos, from the collection of Dr. S. K. St. Joseph, which give a new appreciation of broads and rivers, heaths and the patterns of agricultural enclosures.

The accounts of plant and animal life, by Mrs. Ruth M. Race, formerly at the Castle Museum, Norwich, describe both the rarities for which the brecks are famous, and those peculiar to the meres, riversides and coastline. She shows that, despite its flat terrain, East Anglia is one of our richest provinces for the well-informed naturalist. Most of John Markham's fine photographic studies of beasts and birds were secured in a relatively small group of Commission plantations—those around Dunwich in Aldewood Forest on the Suffolk coast, but all these creatures, and many more besides, can be encountered by the keen explorer in most of the larger woodlands.

In his review of Antiquities and History, Mr. R. Rainbird Clarke formerly Curator of the Castle Museum, Norwich, covers the whole region in a fascinating review of human settlement, from the early Stone Age hunters to the Anglo-Saxon and Scandinavian settlers whose descendants people the region today. He tells where you should look for the remarkable relics of the past that show how people have lived, in the varied patterns of successive cultures, over the past 10,000 years.

Against this pageant of history the great pinewoods, created by foresters within a single life-span, fall into perspective as a recent development of East Anglia's rural economy. But they have an assured future, being already accepted as one of the region's distinctive attractions. Once you have discovered them, you are sure to return, for their evergreen character makes them beautiful places to visit at every season of the year. These pages aim to show you how to gain the fullest enjoyment from these thriving forests and their fascinating surrounding countryside.

Thetford Priory

THETFORD FOREST

BY GEORGE W. BACKHOUSE

THETFORD FOREST is the largest in England. Its beginnings date from 1922, when the first land at Swaffham was acquired and from this small start the area has been built up to a grand total of 51,500 acres, that is roughly 20,800 hectares or 80 square miles. The acquisition of such a vast area was made possible because of the depressed state of the agriculture between the wars. Almost the whole of the area covered by the forest has been under some form of cultivation at one time or another but, prior to acquisition by the Forestry Commission, vast areas had deteriorated into grass heath and much was merely cultivated for short periods of a few years and then left fallow for similar periods. This widespread depression in agriculture produced great poverty in Breckland. Tenants were not easy to find for the farms which became vacant. Few farm hands were employed and they, often, only part time. Many farmers had recourse to rabbit farming; the pelts found a ready market in the fur felt factories in Brandon and the carcases in London. Small wonder that owners were only too willing to

4

Plate I.   Douglas fir plantation at West Tofts, near Thetford. C3603

Plate 2. A forest clearing. Where pines were felled, replanting will follow. Fifty-year-old larches on the right, pines beyond. B5468

Plate 3. Logs are drawn to the roadside and measured. Pine trees stand on the left, larches on the right. B5448

Plate 4. Santon Downham Forest Village, near Brandon. Mature Scots pines shade the green. C4539

Plate 5. Five Stones Plantation, in the Dunwich Woods of Aldewood Forest, Suffolk. Replanted clearing with pinewoods beyond.

Plate 6. Old Scots pines in Brandon Park, near Brandon, Suffolk, with natural
seedlings growing up beneath.

Plate 7. Warren Lodge, the remains of a small fourteenth century two-storeyed hunting lodge, west of Thetford. C4545

Plate 8. The Long Water near Lynford Hall, Mundford: Swamp cypress and two Corsican pines. C3617

Plate 9. Sunlit avenue of limes, near Santon Downham. A2236

Plate 10. Scouten Mere: willows and reedbeds, the haunt of coypus

Plate 11. Sunset over the Dunwich Woodlands on the Suffolk coast

Plate 12. A young plantation of Hybrid poplar, *Populus* 'Serotina', on a fertile drained fen

dispose of their lands to the young Forest Service. Today the picture is quite different; agriculture generally is enjoying prosperity and Breckland has its fair share of this and it is interesting to note that Norfolk possesses more tractors per thousand acres than any other county in the United Kingdom. New techniques of managing the light land, together with the breeding of new strains of corn, have revolutionized farming in the region and there is little doubt that but for the existence of the forest today the whole area would be under agricultural crops. This is a sobering thought for all who, quite understandably, regret the disappearance of so much of the old brecks or heaths.

THE SETTING

The forest occupies a tract of gently undulating land which at the highest point is only 183 feet above sea level and falls to 10 feet above sea level where it merges into the fen on the western side. Because of the growth of the plantations extensive panoramic views are virtually non-existent and indeed it is most difficult for the casual visitor to appreciate the vastness of the forest. Perhaps the best view is from Gallows Hill on the main Thetford/King's Lynn road, a mile or so out of Thetford itself.

Three gently flowing rivers traverse the area from east to west; they are the Wissey, Little Ouse and the Lark. They pass through wide valleys in which, in spite of greatly improved drainage in recent years, considerable areas of carr or fen lands still exist.

The soils of the forest vary from deep sands to very shallow sands always over the chalk. These soils are always freely drained. There are fairly extensive areas which previous to afforestation were blown sand and even today sandblow from adjacent agricultural land can produce unpleasant conditions for people working nearby.

Rainfall averages 23 inches per annum and periods of severe drought are not uncommon. Almost invariably a dry period occurs in the early spring, often combined with searing east winds just at a time when the newly planted trees are least able to withstand these conditions. To this is added the extreme heat of summer when the Breck becomes parched and almost uniformly brown. To the forester these conditions are bad enough but the most serious adverse factor is undoubtedly the regular occurrence of unseasonable frosts in the spring and autumn. Ground frost can occur every month in the year and indeed a year without a frost which causes some damage to tree and plant life is one to be remembered.

These adverse climatic conditions, added to a poor soil, have

5

quite naturally had a deciding influence on the choice of tree species used in the earlier plantings. Such a species must be able to tolerate unseasonable frosts and conditions of drought which can be severe and survive the high summer temperatures. It was natural, therefore, that Scots pine should be the species most extensively used in these earlier years since there was ample evidence, in the locality, that it could withstand these conditions and grow to produce good timber. Another pine, Corsican pine, was used to a less extent but proved much more difficult to establish; of this species more later.

Other species of conifer used included Douglas fir and European larch. Again both were found less tolerant of the adverse conditions and were later extensively replaced by pine. Of the broadleaved species oak and beech were far more widely used than the present plantations suggest. Beech, in mixture with larch or pine, which helped to protect this tender species against frost and drought, was extensively used on soils shallow over the chalk. Oak, again in mixture, was used on the better soils particularly on the eastern side of the forest. Failure to establish oak and beech successfully was due to a combination of the adverse climatic conditions and to serious grazing by hares and roe deer.

PLANTING AND PROTECTION

In the early years the forester's tasks consisted of fencing new areas to be planted, clearing the enclosed areas of rabbits—82,312 rabbits were taken from one typical area of 6,000 acres—planting, weeding the young trees and protecting them from their many enemies, not the least of which was fire.

Plants were raised in one of the many nurseries within the forest boundary. This process began by collecting cones of Scots pine, acorns and beech mast from the old hedgerows and woodlands. Scots pine seed was extracted from the cones in the special plant then located at Santon Downham but since dismantled. The next stage was to sow the seed in the nursery where, after two years, the seedlings were lifted and lined out for another year or possibly two. The young tree was then ready to go out into the forest and when planting was at its height some 200 acres of nursery annually produced some 7 million transplants.

The technique of planting on the open land was to plough a shallow single furrow and to notch in the small tree in the bottom of the furrow. A man could plant 1,500 trees in a day. Costs were low and indeed over extensive areas the whole cost of fencing, clearing rabbits, ploughing and planting, including the cost of plants, averaged £4.50 per acre!

The plantations themselves were divided into blocks averaging 25 acres and separated by wide rides for access and fire protection. Belts of broadleaved species of trees were planted along each and every road within the forest with the double purpose of breaking up the blocks of conifers and hence limiting the spread of fire and also to provide amenity. Most of these broadleaved belts survive today and are a great feature of the roads throughout the forest.

The pine plantations, both Scots and Corsican pine, were generally successful but Douglas fir and European larch only in those areas relatively free from unseasonable frosts. The success of the broadleaved species varied greatly; some did not survive the adverse conditions even after repeated replanting and were eventually replaced by pine, others survived but did not grow well until the nurse species had provided complete shelter—often not until ten years had passed. A limited area of broadleaved belts planted in the more frost-free sites grew successfully from the start, particularly near roads where traffic tended to keep the deer and hares away.

During the years when the plantations were growing up, and the forest area was being extended, fire protection became of paramount importance. Look-out towers, five in number, were built by local staff and manned in periods of high fire danger. Cycle patrols augmented this constant watch. A particularly vulnerable zone was that traversed by the mainline railway, then operated by steam locomotives. In spite of the precautions numerous fires did occur and unfortunately a few caused serious loss of plantations. With the advent of diesel engines on this route losses from this cause almost ceased. Some roads were constructed to facilitate access by fire-fighting vehicles, but it was not until after the war that the present extensive network of roads was laid down.

Fire is not the only risk to which the plantations have been subjected. Various insect pests are an ever present threat. In the early years the Pine shoot moth (*Evetria buoliana*) caused serious damage and even today the results of this may be seen in the typical 'post horn' deformation of the stems of the Scots pine.

Weevils and beetles of several species have given trouble in the past and even today all new plantations have to be sprayed with a suitable insecticide to prevent damage during the first few years. Of fungus diseases by far the most serious is *Fomes annosus*, known to every one in the forest simply as 'Fomes'. It gains entry via the stumps of trees which have been felled, grows down through the root system thence into the roots of living trees and eventually kills these. Evidence of the ravages of 'Fomes' are to be seen here

7

and there in groups of dead trees. Control was for a number of years effected by sterilising the surface of the cut stump by application of creosote, but lately by means of introducing into the dead stump another fungus (*Peniophora giganteu*) which keeps out the Fomes and is not itself a tree killer. Both these forms of control, now widely used in forests throughout many parts of the world, were pioneered here. Indeed, this forest has been the location of much valuable research work, not only in the establishment and protection of plantations, but in the problems of large-scale harvesting and conversion of timber.

Even the most far-seeing of the earlier foresters could hardly have visualised the forest as we find it today. Magnificent plantations stretch as far as the eye can see and a drive through the forest cannot fail to impress one with the excellent plantations to be seen everywhere. The general impression is one of a well-managed and thriving undertaking which has made excellent use of the poor land and produces a sight which gladdens the eye.

In spite of severe losses of land, much of which was already planted with trees, to the Service Departments both during and after the war, the total area of the forest now stands at 51,500 acres (20,800 hectares) of which 90 per cent is under plantations. Nurseries now occupy a mere 57 acres (22 hectares), and the only one of any size is highly mechanized. This latter nursery can be seen stretching along the railway line to the north of the main A.11 road where it crosses Bridgham Heath, five miles north-east from Thetford town.

THINNING

The appearance of the plantations has changed tremendously even in the last fifteen years. They have moved out of the 'care and maintenance' stage and become a highly productive forest. The first stage in this process was to brash the trees at an age of 16 to 20 years. This consists of cutting off all branches to a height of 6 feet and provides easy access for the next step, which is thinning. The original plantations contained about 2,000 plants per acre and at the time of brashing the number has usually been reduced to something like 1,500 by natural losses; these survivors must progressively be thinned out, firstly to remove misshapen and damaged trees and secondly to give the remaining trees more room to develop until at economic maturity, which is approximately 60 years, only 150 or so trees remain standing on each acre of land.

In this forest the thinning process has been put on a systematic basis perhaps more so than anywhere in the United Kingdom.

8

Thinning begins at about the eighteenth year, the second follows four years later and the third after a similar period and so on. Thinning in any one year is concentrated in a limited number of widely dispersed but well defined blocks and hence the whole forest is systematically worked over every fourth year. In a normal year some 6,000 acres (2,400 hectares) of forest are covered and, of course, ultimately this will rise to one fourth of it (or twice the present rate). The first stage in the thinning process is to completely remove two rows of trees across the whole compartment at intervals of some 40 yards. The space so cleared, known as a rack, provides access for tractors and also room to stack the poles cut in the thinnings.

HARVESTING TIMBER

The selection of trees to be cut is the responsibility of the skilled gangers under the guidance of the foresters. The forest workers then move in and the plantation quickly becomes a hive of activity. The power saw with its staccato note has now completely replaced the old hand saw and axe. In the earlier thinnings of young crops the felling gang carry out the smaller poles to the racks and tractors quickly follow behind and deal with the larger materials; but in later thinnings, involving larger trees, all material is extracted by tractor. Lorries equipped with grapples quickly follow behind the felling gang and either transport the material direct to a local factory or to the central conversion depot situated close to the Railway Station at Brandon. Alternatively, the lorries are mechanically loaded for journeys to more distant places.

A fleet of 21 lorries owned by the Forestry Commission is employed on this work and the whole process from tree-stump to selling point is entirely the work of the local staff.

The timber conversion depot at Brandon now extends to 38 acres and is by far the largest and busiest of its kind in the country. In it all material produced in the forest which cannot be despatched direct to the consumer is processed. Annually the forest produces 125,000 cubic metres (each equivalent to one ton or metric tonne) of timber and of this some two-thirds passes through the conversion depot. By 1985 the total production will have risen to 140,000 cubic metres annually.

Markets for this timber fluctuate greatly from year to year. At the time of writing (1971) 17,000 tons or roughly one-sixth of the overall production is converted into pitprops for the National Coal Board for use in mines as far afield as South Wales and Durham. About 42,000 tons, or roughly one-third, goes to the sawmilling industry and the remainder to various factories for conversion into paper

9

pulp, hardboard, particle board and woodwool which is used for packaging. Large quantities of fencing posts and poles for special purposes are also produced. The whole picture is one of a thriving forest industry.

RESTOCKING FELLED WOODLANDS

In order to even-out production over a long period, and to avoid very large areas of the forest becoming mature and hence requiring felling at one time, a programme of clear felling has been in force since 1963 and is now averaging 600 acres (240 hectares) per year. As the cut in one place rarely exceeds 75 acres (30 hectares), the general appearance of the forest will not change significantly. The task of restocking the felled areas has proved far more difficult than establishing the original plantations. It would be far too expensive to remove the stumps of the trees and these are left to rot. The heavy mass of branch wood and tree tops is left to dry out for at least one summer and is then chopped by a flail-type of machine which produces conditions whereby ploughing, as for the first crop, can be carried out. Generally nowadays much wider planting spacing is adopted than previously. Usually when clear felling an area groups of trees are left standing. The purpose of this is largely for amenity, to preserve the woodland views.

Weed growth in the newly-formed plantations is now largely controlled by chemicals, or by tractor-drawn machines.

Whereas in the original plantations Scots pine was used to an extent of something like 75 per cent by area, and Corsican pine about 20 per cent, in the replanting Corsican pine is used more extensively. The reason for this is that, as compared with Scots pine, it grows much faster, matures earlier and over its rotation period produces almost double the volume of timber as does Scots pine.

The idea of clear felling and replanting may surprise those more familiar with the Continental practice of natural regeneration, where the trees are encouraged to restock the area with seed falling from selected trees left standing, but this is in fact the more practical and economic approach. However, where natural regeneration can be achieved cheaply and quickly, and the existing trees are of good quality, it would be accepted. An excellent example of natural regeneration is to be found in the beautiful Brandon Park area, where several hundred acres have been regenerated and indeed parts are now in their third rotation. Where regeneration cannot be obtained cheaply, and this applies to the bulk of the forest, replanting provides the best solution and enables

10

more use to be made of improved strains of all species and, of course, extended use of Corsican pine.

The total staff of forest workers varies around 300 men, including tractor drivers, lorry drivers and men employed on the maintenance of machinery of all kinds. The majority of workers are highly skilled and paid accordingly. Of these workers some 128 live in Forestry Commission houses scattered around the forest. The new village of Santon Downham is one of the largest concentrations of Forestry Commission houses, and is a model of which even the lovely county of Suffolk may well be proud. In all there are 330 houses owned by the Forestry Commission within the forest's boundary. The more isolated of these, particularly where modern amenities are never likely to be available, are let as weekend cottages to city dwellers in search of a peaceful country retreat.

The care of these houses and other property is the responsibility of the Clerks of Works, and much repair work is in fact done by Forestry Commission staff.

The fleet of lorries and tractors, together with such items as saw benches, cranes, pumps and many other machines are the responsibility of the Engineer and his staff at Santon Downham.

The estate and engineering staff, together with the forest management staff, are located in the old village of Santon Downham. This administrative centre has recently been rebuilt to architect's design, using wood to the maximum extent possible. It is an excellent example of what an understanding architect can do with timber. The staff here is always ready to give advice and help to all interested in the forest or in forestry. It is from here, too, that the organizations for fire detection, and actual fire fighting are controlled. The fire control centre at Santon Downham is highly organized; Forestry Commission fire tenders can be sent out within minutes of a warning being received and all key vehicles are fitted with short-wave radio.

The wild life of the forest has changed greatly since the first plantings took place, but this was inevitable. However since felling of plantations has been going on signs have been noted of the return of some of the bird life which used to exist here. Where rare, or even unusual plants, are known to exist every effort is made to preserve them.

Within the forest red squirrels are common and indeed it is one of the last major strongholds in the south of England. Grey squirrels are not present in the depth of the forest but have penetrated the borders to the south. Three species of deer have lived in the forest for many years; red, roe and fallow. Recently a fourth species has appeared, the muntjac which is presumed to have reached the forest from the original point of introduction in Bedfordshire. Roe deer are the commonest and numbers are controlled to prevent serious damage to young trees by browsing and rubbing.

RECREATION   (See map, rear endpapers)

In running this large commercial undertaking, sight has not been lost of the forest's great value to the public for recreational purposes. Indeed it is the Forestry Commission's declared policy to develop the recreational potential to the fullest extent, bearing in mind the primary objective of production of timber. The number of visitors increases annually; at present most are day visitors and for these the main requirement is picnic places with ample space to park. Ten picnic places exist at the present but these are being added to each year; of these some are small and intimate but most are much larger and have ample room for children to play.

Two Nature Trails have been laid out, one commencing at the forest office at West Stow and the other from the forest centre at Santon Downham. They consist of a signposted route together with a simple booklet explaining points of interest along the route, and are much used by young and old but particularly by parties of school children. With most picnic places are associated forest walks which are simply a signposted route through the woods, returning to the same point. They are usually in pairs, a short stroll and a longer one for the more energetic.

For the walking enthusiast a long distance walk of twenty-three miles has been laid out. The starting places are shown on the plan and again the route is clearly marked on the ground. Ample car parking space is provided at each end.

A small caravan park has existed for some years in the Mildenhall Woods and in 1967 a much larger caravan-cum-camping site was opened at High Ash on the Didlington Beat. Both these are run by the Caravan Club but the High Ash site is not confined to members.

In the spring of 1971 it is intended to develop two larger recreational centres. The one at Lynford includes a stretch of ornamental water, a delightful arboretum covering 16 acres, together with pleasant walks through the mixed plantations in what were once the pleasure grounds of Lynford Hall. Again ample space for cars is provided. The second development is at Thorpe Farm, Harling an area of 60 acres running down to the River Thet and here a small lake is being created; fifty caravan sites will be made available and ultimately it is intended to provide space for campers. This site

12

will take a number of years to develop fully but it has great potential.

Two camping sites are administered by the Norfolk and West Suffolk Education Authorities for organized parties. A small public camp site has been opened at East Harling (see page 78), and no doubt more will be provided as the demand evinces itself.

During the Forestry Commission's Jubilee Year—1969—an old estate building at Santon Downham was adapted as a public information centre. It contains displays of forest activities and the wild life of the area. From the centre one may buy a simple guide map showing the main points of interest in the forest, guides for the two Nature Trails, together with a variety of leaflets on woodland animals generally.

Much of the forest can be enjoyed from public roads, footpaths and bridleways. However the whole forest is open to the public except where restrictive covenants with lessors prevents this. Thus the public may wander at will along the vast network of rides provided always that they behave themselves. In the interests of the public motor vehicles are not permitted on the private roads; the aim is to keep the forest peaceful for all to enjoy. Visitors must always bear in mind that over the whole forest the sporting is let and hence they should avoid disturbing game, particularly in the nesting season. It is for this reason that dogs are only allowed in the forest if on leash and under strict control.

Favourite walks in the forest are many but the following are outstanding:

(1) The tow-path along the Little Ouse from Brandon to Thetford, with a break at Santon Downham if required.

(2) Across the Thetford Golf Course, past the so-called Leper's Lodge, into the forest, keeping left along the fire route 8 below Barrow Hill and on to the main A.11 road; thence back to Thetford.

(3) The old Harling Drove, which enters the main block of the forest on the east side near Langmere, and leaves it on the west side one mile out of Brandon down the Mundford road.

(4) The lovely Icknield Way which passes through the King's Forest from the northern tip to Lackford village.

(5) The Pilgrims' Walk from Weeting to Cranwich.

(6) Santon Downham to Santon past St. Helen's Well to gain the Thetford-Swaffham road.

(7) Bridgham Lane at Harling with access to River Thet.

These are but a few of an endless number of walks enjoyed by increasing numbers of people each year. Everywhere in the forest one will see beauty and enjoy peace. In the spring and autumn in particular the forest is a riot of colour, a heavenly place to be in. May it always be so!

Thetford Warren seen from Gallows Hill

The River Alde at Ikencliff near Aldeburgh

ALDEWOOD FOREST IN SUFFOLK

BY GEORGE W. BACKHOUSE

T HE plantations which make up the forest of Aldewood are situated on the infertile heathland which stretches from Woodbridge to Southwold, backed on the one side by the sea and on the other by the rich wheatlands of East Suffolk. There are three main blocks, known as Rendlesham, Tunstall and Dunwich and there are a number of small outlying woods attached to each of these forests. One of these outliers, Waveney, lies on the bank of the river of that name and just behind Great Yarmouth.

The climate is similar to that at Thetford; rainfall is slightly lower and there is the same trouble with unseasonable frosts.

The underlying rock here is not the chalk as at Thetford but much younger rocks known as the Norwich and Red Crags and Chillesford Clays, together with a strip of the Coralline Crag. Soils generally are deep sands, occasionally with hard gravel beds and some clay. Generally the soils are acid.

Previous to acquisition by the Forestry Commission the great part of the land was heathland, with great stretches of bracken or heather and grass. Most had been used for sheep grazing but,

15

unlike Thetford, little had been under cultivation except for limited areas around the old farmsteads themselves.

The first acquisition by the Forestry Commission was in 1920 and amounted to 2,544 acres of land at Tangham. This was quickly followed by others until today the total area is:

Rendlesham	3,958 acres
Tunstall	3,064 acres
Dunwich	1,650 acres
Waveney	292 acres
Total	8,964 acres (3,600 hectares, or about 14 square miles)

During the war years, from 1939 to 1945, a large part of Tunstall forest was taken over for military training and two airfields were constructed largely on land which had already been planted with trees. One of these—Woodbridge Airfield—virtually severs the Rendlesham plantations in two. Apart from these airfields the ravages of wartime occupation have largely been healed.

The establishment of the plantation closely followed the pattern described at Thetford—fencing, extermination of rabbits, single furrow ploughing, planting, weeding and so on but here much greater use was made of Corsican pine even in the earliest years, though Scots pine was still the most widely planted species. Some oak was planted on the old arable land but has not been very successful and has now largely been replaced. Poplar was extensively planted in the wet valleys but unfortunately most trees fell prey to canker. They have now been cut and the land replanted.

It is interesting to note that Maritime pine (*Pinus pinaster*) was sown on some 200 acres. Most of this produced a crop, but though visually very attractive, from the timber point of view it was not very satisfactory; hence it has now been felled and replaced by Corsican pine.

As at Thetford, Douglas fir was also used to a small extent; some trees still survive, forming very attractive plantations over limited areas.

Thinning is carried out as already described for Thetford and total annual production is 17,000 cubic metres (roughly equivalent to 17,000 tons or metric tonnes) of timber. There is no fixed conversion depot at Aldewood and the work is done on broad rides within each thinning block. The produce is disposed of in the same markets as that from Thetford; sawlogs, woodwool and pulp. Almost the whole output is processed by Commission staff.

Clearfelling of Corsican pine plantations which are economically mature has now commenced and is proceeding at the rate of some twenty-five acres each year.

The total staff employed is around forty-five, many of whom live in Forestry Commission houses scattered around the forest and in neighbouring villages.

The wild life of the forest includes red squirrels and fallow deer, while the red deer are occasional visitors. There are also small numbers of hares and rabbits. The smaller blocks of plantations are rich in bird life and those at Dunwich in particular owe much to the proximity of the sea, marshes and extensive areas of heathland.

In the past the two larger blocks of plantation were not greatly frequented by the public but each year ever-increasing numbers enjoy the peace and quiet of the lovely woods. At Dunwich however the position has always been different. Running down almost to the seashore it provides a welcome haven for visitors when the wind is in the east. Those who know the East Anglian coast when the wind is in this quarter need no further elaboration!

Several picnic places have existed for some years and are well used. As demand increases so new ones are and will continue to be provided. Ample space for parking cars is available on all picnic sites and most have a waymarked forest walk attached. No public caravan site exists as yet but the summer of 1972 should see an establishment at Dunwich. This will be a 'minimum facilities' site at first but will be converted to a 'full facilities' site later. Two more public caravan-cum-camping sites will be opened in successive years. A camping site at Tunstall is run by the East Suffolk County Council for organized parties, and is much used.

There are many delightful walks in the forest which visitors can enjoy. Regrettably the woodlands are often far from peaceful because of the activity of planes from the two airfields. When peace reigns these forests are a joy to anyone who is prepared to walk.

The remaining forests in East Suffolk are composed of scattered woodlands which have been acquired by the Forestry Commission during the last fifteen years. The plantations are, therefore, quite young and for the most part are in the uninteresting thicket stage. In time they will contribute significantly to the amenities and landscape of East Anglia. However, some woods are well worth a visit today. Among these are Arger Fen, with its rich vegetation situated some two miles north-east of Bures, Assington Thicks close to the village of Assington and two miles north of Arger Fen, Stanstead Great Wood and Lineage Wood both three miles north-west and north-east respectively of Long Melford. All are readily accessible to those prepared to walk.

17

Weybourne Heath, near Sheringham, looking seawards

NORTH NORFOLK FORESTS:
LYNN AND WENSUM

BY G. F. BALLANCE

HISTORY

When one looks at the map of England the county of Norfolk is situated in that part where the greatest land mass occurs; the first impressions therefore are that the land utilization should have developed over the centuries along the national pattern. On closer investigation however one finds that the county of Norfolk has been virtually detached from the rest of the kingdom until relatively recent times.

One finds the natural boundary of the sea on the north and east sides of the county and to the west the extensive and largely impassable marshes of the Fenland. While to the south lay the often flooded rivers and marshlands of the Waveney and Thet rivers. Thus the only sound link with the rest of the country for many centuries lay across the wild Breckland country in the south-west corner of the county.

Norfolk in its isolation was left, with a few noteworthy exceptions, undisturbed by the reaction and internal strife which have beset the kingdom over the last thousand years and in particular during the Middle Ages. Civilization developed steadily around the village community to a sort of benevolent feudalism with the big landlords or squires owning large estates and maintaining the village populations.

Agriculture was the principal occupation and all worthwhile land was given over to this use but sporting for game birds has long been a traditional pastime and the poorer land on each estate was adapted for this purpose and maintained as woodland or scrubland.

At intervals through the centuries, with the pressure to employ soldiers returning from the wars or actual prisoners of war, efforts were made to plant up and tend these woodlands.

There was nowhere a continuous block of forest, the woodlands seldom exceeding 300 acres. To the north-east of the county however some tracts of very poor land north of Norwich and on the Cromer Ridge (Plate 13) carried a scattering of naturally regenerated Scots pine, the common land being used for summer sheep grazing.

So firmly rooted are the customs and traditions of these big estates that even today after two World Wars and with the advent of modern communications they remain the foundation of the county's rural economy. It is not surprising therefore that the advent of the Forestry Commission in 1919 made little impact on the county outside Breckland and it was not until 1929 that the first acquisition of land occurred near Swanton Novers. The area involved was only some 450 acres (100 hectares) and although a few additional nearby areas were added the total Forestry Commission activities were limited to about 800 acres (320 hectares) until after the Second World War.

During this second war very considerable areas of woodland were felled in the national interest, leaving extensive but individually small areas of derelict woodland which the estate owners could no longer afford to maintain. With the intensive post-war programme of reafforestation and acquisition many of these areas were taken over by the Forestry Commission either by purchase or long lease. Today the forest estate administered by the Forestry Commission amounts to nearly 8,000 acres (3,200 hectares).

THE NORFOLK FORESTS

For operational purposes these numerous scattered woodlands and plantations are grouped into two forests—Wensum and Lynn. *Wensum Forest* extends over the eastern half of the county and in total covers an area of 5,200 acres (2,080 hectares) made up of 40 separate blocks. The name is taken from the well-known river, which with its tributaries, is a major feature of the countryside. For local administration the forest is divided into four sections, Swanton, Hevingham, Holt and Walsham, these being named after the communities forming the focal centres of the Section. *Lynn Forest* comprising 2,700 acres (1,080 hectares) is situated in the western part of the county within a twelve-mile radius of King's Lynn, whence it derives its name. It is divided into two sections, Shouldham to the south around the market village and old warren of that name and Gaywood to the north called after the local river. Seventeen separate woodland blocks make up this forest.

19

With such widely scattered forests one would expect a great diversity of ground conditions and such is indeed so. The country-side is generally flat with only slight undulations, there being an almost complete absence of marked topographical features. Ele-vations are negligible except on the Cromer ridge where they rise to about 400 feet and give a few steep slopes on the seaward side. The county is exposed not only to the prevailing south-west winds but also to gales from the north and east coming off the open sea.

In a mainly agricultural area, the woodland sites are almost entirely on the poorer soils. At Wensum Forest there are very extensive areas of hard gravels with little sand, although individual blocks and parts of the Swanton section contain some heavier loams and generally mellower soils.

Large parts of Lynn Forest are situated on a narrow belt of Greensand while gravelly loams predominate elsewhere. One cannot call any of the forest soils encountered very fertile but on the whole they are admirably suited to tree growth.

As the Forestry Commission acquired the North Norfolk areas they fell heir to large areas of devastated scrub with a proportion of young poles of various hardwoods. Birch, and to a lesser extent ash, elm, alder and oak with some beech and sweet chestnut, occurred sporadically in pole size. Many stems originated from the coppice which existed under a previous stand of large timber trees. On the more open heathland sites the relics of bygone grazing—birch had colonized the ground, and to a lesser extent Scots pine.

The ground vegetation also is varied. On the true old woodland sites brambles and briars, with mixed grasses and other soft vegeta-tion, predominate, while the more open tracts carry a crop of bracken and heather, also in association with grasses, among which *Molinia coerulea* and *Holcus mollis* predominate.

PLANTATIONS

Many of the sites now forming parts of Wensum and Lynn Forests carried timber crops of oak, elm, ash, alder and other hardwoods, with some Scots pine and a few introduced Douglas fir and Silver fir.

In the earlier years planting included a rather wider range of species than had been used in the breckland. More use was made of oak, both planted pure and in mixture with such exotic species as Western red cedar and Lawson cypress. However many of these plantations did not succeed and were later replaced by pines; but relics of these broadleaved plantations do survive particularly in the form of belts and add greatly to the beauty of the forests.

Pines, both Scots and Corsican, were extensively used even in the earliest years. They proved most successful and these species are now the main species planted, with Corsican in the majority.

Apart from the small area of 30-year-old plantations near Swanton Novers, all the Forestry Commission woodlands are in a young stage, but many are already taking their place in the amenities of the county. One does not get the panoramic effect of great sweeping forests, but one cannot travel far through the county without becoming aware of thriving new plantations.

It is perhaps fitting that it should be this way. Norfolk has developed on the strength of its village communities with their many attractions and points of artistic merit and the picture is well filled-in with a background of small but productive woodlands.

FOREST OPERATIONS

The forester practising his skill in Norfolk will find little to confront him which is not recorded somewhere in his training textbooks. His problems hinge far more on adapting his work and programmes to the very important local factors which can affect his results. Factors such as drought, frost, wind, and the seasons of the year, all of which he has learnt about, can in this region become the dominating feature in his work for long spells at a time.

Careful planning with maximum flexibility is essential and when this is fully appreciated all aspects of forest work can be successfully carried out. The very earliest stage is that of the forest nursery for the production of the young trees to plant out in the woods.

Clearing of scrub growth, ploughing of the soil, fencing against rabbits and sometimes drainage are all necessary preliminaries to the actual planting out of the trees. After planting the young trees require weeding to remove the competing ground vegetation and later pruning to remove the lower dead branches. All this leads up to the thinning stage, which can begin about the eighteenth year, and then the forest produce starts coming out. At the two forests of Lynn and Wensum forty men are regularly employed on such tasks.

The outturn from the forests today is about 60,000 cubic metres of poles and small timber, which is used as sawlogs for planks, pitprops, stakes, pulpwood and woodwool. With the rapid development of the plantations this will grow to a substantially larger figure during the next decade. (1 cubic metre equals 1 ton or metric tonne of fresh-felled timber.)

FOREST PROTECTION

Both Wensum and Lynn Forests are subject to many pests and

21

diseases which affect our forests, both insect and fungi, but by careful attention to known methods of control and protection these are kept within tolerable limits. Rabbits however continue to be a constant source of damage and endless efforts on the part of the foresters are needed to keep their numbers down.

A small herd of Fallow deer roam the woodlands in the general area of Wensum forest but do not occasion any serious damage. On Lynn forest one can occasionally come across a very few white Fallow deer. These originated at the Houghton Estate and have now settled in the forest and neighbouring woods.

Grey squirrels are inexorably colonizing what has been for many years one of the few zones free of this pest in England. There seems little to halt this but concerted action by all landowners could slow-up their further spread considerably.

By far the greatest risk to the plantations is from fire, which due to the very dry climate can be a great hazard in spring and summer when vegetation becomes dry. With the big influx of visitors and holiday makers in recent years the casual cigarette or well intentioned picnic fire can give rise to very serious losses. These losses are not only the immediate value of what is destroyed but the loss of time involved in growing a new plantation to replace that burnt out.

RECREATION

The forests are playing an ever-increasing role in providing facilities for public recreation, limited only by sporting interests on land which is leased to the Forestry Commission by private owners. A delightful forest walk has been opened at Bacton Wood, the most easterly block of all. More picnic places and forest walks are planned for opening shortly.

CONCLUSION

Much has been written and more said about the mutual advantages of forestry and agriculture working together in the hill country of the North of Britain; but it is perhaps in the county of Norfolk that such cooperation may be seen to the best advantage. The quiet but steady development of useful and pleasing plantations and woodlands in Wensum and Lynn Forests, together with the enterprise on private estates, gives a picture of rural wellbeing and wise use of land. Although none of the woodland blocks are really large the fact that truly successful forestry is working in close co-operation with agriculture and sporting, to the benefit of all, is a matter of which foresters can feel truly proud.

Added to the purely economic aspects are the advantages of

amenity and recreation in which Wensum and Lynn Forests play no small part, making Norfolk one of the nicest counties in which to 'get away from it all'.

Reedbeds, South Walsham Broad

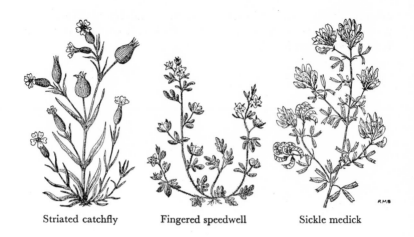

| Striated catchfly | Fingered speedwell | Sickle medick |

PLANT LIFE

BY RUTH M. RACE

INTRODUCTION

Although East Anglia consists of lowland, nearly all below the 300-foot contour, and includes a large proportion of land which has been farmed or otherwise modified by human activities through the centuries, it nevertheless supports a highly interesting and varied wild flora. In the west there is Breckland, unique for its dry climate and shallow, light soils with relict 'steppe' plants. In the east, the Broads, with their fens and reedswamps, are the refuge of rare species not found elsewhere in Britain. The coast dunes and salt-marshes are also of outstanding interest for the number of species rare or absent in other parts of this country. In addition to these three main botanical regions, there are Greensand heaths and Chalk uplands in the west, bordering the Fens. The central area of Norfolk and Suffolk is, broadly speaking, a low plateau covered with boulder clays and largely agricultural, but with indigenous communities of plants surviving in the river valleys, meadows, commons and small deciduous woodlands. Some sandy country in north-east Norfolk and east Suffolk typically carries heathland vegetation and well suited to the growing of pine and birch. Tracts of damp heathland and bog, associated with the Greensand belt, the Breck sands and glacial sands in the east, are often rich in rare or unusual plants.

The largest Commission plantations are in Breckland, so the vegetation of this region will be dealt with here in detail. Close

24

Plate 13. Aerial view of wooded heathlands on morainic deposits inland from Cromer, looking north-west towards the town and the sea. PU4

Plate 14. Brandon, Suffolk, seen from the air, looking north. N277

Plate 15. Thetford, Norfolk, seen from the south. Note the castle mound. PT13

Plate 16. Aerial view of Weeting Heath Nature Reserve, two miles north-west of Brandon. Large open arable fields, grass heath, young Forestry Commission plantations, older private woodlands. In the left middle distance, patterns in grass heath reflect periglacial disturbance of underlying soil. WI82

Plate 17. Fowlmere, four miles north of Thetford, one of several local meres in which water levels rise or fall in relation to regional water-table in the underlying chalk. VS78

Plate 18. The track of a vanished river, or 'roddon' revealed by crop markings in an aerial view of the Fens, south-east of Littleport, Isle of Ely. Farmsteads are often sited on silty deposits of roddons since they give more stable foundations, than do peats. Note large arable fields bounded by drainage ditches. WL2

Plate 19. Surlingham Broad and the River Yare, Norfolk. Showing re-colonization by swamp vegetation of the original open water of the broad. Note well-drained farmland nearby. ADD94

Plate 20. Typical enclosure pattern on this light-textured drift overlying the chalk. Each field holds its marl pit from which calcareous drift or chalk was once dug for liming. XU52

attention will also be given to the east Suffolk fens and coast adjoining Aldewood Forest. There are few plantations near the north Norfolk marshland coast and the Broads, but a few of the more outstanding features of botanical interest in these areas will be included in this account.

BRECKLAND HEATHS AND FORESTS

Unique features of this region are its low rainfall, continental type of climate (with 'frost pockets') and the 'steppe' element in the flora. Several coast plants, such as sand sedge (*Carex arenaria*) are present. Formerly this was an area of extensive open sandy heaths, where sheep and rabbits grazed freely and cropped the turf so closely as to prevent most tree growth. With the afforestation of Thetford Chase the rarer species characteristic of Breckland have diminished and are now to be found mainly in the Nature Reserves. Large areas of open heath remain, however, in the country retained for the use of army training units, while the forest rides, firebreaks and roadside verges also provide refuges for wild vegetation.

Travelling through Breckland by rail or road, the visitor has an impression of a vast expanse of conifer forest stretching into the distance like a grey-green sea. The dense canopy of the pines and the deep litter of pine needles on the ground virtually exclude other forms of vegetation; only at the margins bracken, brambles and tall grasses suddenly come into prominence. Some broad vistas of open breck remain and particularly in the battle training area it is still possible to enjoy the impression of limitless space typical of the whole region before afforestation.

In summer, roadside banks and tracks are bright with flowers, including lady's bedstraw (*Galium verum*), wild mignonette (*Reseda lutea*), musk mallow (*Malva moschata*), rest-harrow (*Ononis repens*), birdsfoot trefoil (*Lotus corniculatus*), ragwort (*Senecio jacobaea*), black mullein (*Verbascum nigrum*), musk thistle (*Carduus nutans*), greater knapweed (*Centaurea scabiosa*) and the charming pink sainfoin (*Onobrychis viciifolia*). Sickle medick (*Medicago falcata*), a rarity outside Breckland, here hybridizes freely with the cultivated lucerne (*M. sativa*) to produce a wide range of variously coloured flowers, from blackish purple to sulphur yellow (*Medicago* x *varia*).

Common plants of sandy brecks and fallow fields are wild thyme (*Thymus* spp.), storksbill (*Erodium cicutarium*), hare's-foot (*Trifolium arvense*), viper's bugloss (*Echium vulgare*), stone-crop (*Sedum acre*), bugloss (*Anchusa arvensis*), flixweed (*Descurainia sophia*) and slender cudweed (*Filago minima*).

On much disturbed land, such as may be found round the edges

25

of gravel pits, one finds dyer's rocket (*Reseda luteola*), great mullein (*Verbascum thapsus*) and hound's-tongue (*Cynoglossum officinale*). The common and white melilots (*Melilotus officinalis* and *alba*) are plentiful on waste land right up to the edges of plantations. Rosebay ('fireweed') willow-herb, (*Epilobium angustifolium*) makes a show where woodland has been cleared and litter burned. Alien invaders include tumbling mustard (*Sisymbrium altissimum*), which first appeared in army camps in the 1914–18 war and is now established and spreading, especially along the railway between Thetford and Brandon; hoary mustard (*Hirschfeldia incana*), established on roadsides at Santon and Weeting since 1957, and the Scotch thistle (*Onopordum acanthium*), now conspicuous along some roadsides.

In places where the underlying chalk comes near the surface, especially in disturbed areas such as chalk pits, railway cuttings, man-made tracks and banks such as the Devil's Dykes and the Icknield Way, numerous chalk-loving plants occur, notably yellow rock-rose (*Helianthemum chamaecistus*), purple milk-vetch (*Astragalus danicus*), ladies' fingers (*Anthyllis vulneraria*), horse-shoe vetch (*Hippocrepis comosa*), salad burnet (*Poterium sanguisorba*), wild parsnip (*Pastinaca sativa*), marjoram (*Origanum vulgare*), dropwort (*Filipendula vulgaris*), purging flax (*Linum catharticum*), squinancy-wort (*Asperula cynanchica*), stemless thistle (*Cirsium acaulon*), small scabious (*Scabiosa columbaria*) and quaking grass (*Briza media*).

The short Breckland turf is rich in spring-flowering annuals, such as whitlow-grass (*Erophila verna*), shepherd's cress (*Teesdalia nudicaulis*), early forget-me-not (*Myosotis ramosissima*), yellow and blue forget-me-not (*M. discolor*), wall speedwell (*Veronica arvensis*), rue-leaved saxifrage (*Saxifraga tridactylites*), bird's-foot (*Ornithopus perpusillus*), spring vetch (*Vicia lathyroides*), smooth cat's-ear (*Hypochoeris glabra*) and hair-grasses (*Aira* spp.). With them grow the perennial field mouse-ear chickweed (*Cerastium arvense*) and sheep's sorrel (*Rumex acetosella*). The rare moonwort fern (*Botrychium lunaria*) appears occasionally in the turf.

White varieties of flowers which are normally pink or purple occur quite frequently in the Breck, especially in the cases of heather (*Calluna vulgaris*), basil-thyme (*Acinos arvensis*), storksbill (*Erodium cicularium*) and wild thyme (*Thymus pulegioides*).

Special Breckland plants are listed below. Those marked with an asterisk are not found in Britain outside East Anglia; the rest are in most instances found in only a very few other localities.

*Spanish catchfly (*Silene otites*)
Striated catchfly (*Silene conica*)
*Field wormwood (*Artemisia campestris*)

Maiden pink (*Dianthus deltoides*)
Small medick (*Medicago minima*)

Spiked speedwell (*Veronica spicata*)
*Spring speedwell (*Veronica verna*)
Fingered speedwell (*Veronica triphyllos*)
*Early speedwell (*Veronica praecox*)
*Wild thyme (*Thymus serpyllum*)

Ground pine (*Ajuga chamaepitys*)
Glabrous rupture-wort (*Herniaria glabra*)
Perennial knawel (*Scleranthus perennis*)
Star-of-Bethlehem (*Ornithogalum umbellatum*)
Grape hyacinth (*Muscari atlanticum*)

Heath sedge (*Carex ericetorum*)
Dense silky bent (*Apera interrupta*)
Bearded fescue (*Vulpia ambigua*)
Purple-stemmed cat's-tail (*Phleum phleoides*)
Narrow small-reed (*Calamagrostis stricta*)—a very rare grass known
    for fifty years at Cranberry Rough, a fen adjacent to the Breck-
    land forest.

Former rarities now extinct in the region were the hairy green-
weed (*Genista pilosa*) which grew on sandy heaths between
Bury and Tuddenham; cat's-foot (*Antennaria dioica*) on heaths at
Cavenham, Culford and Newmarket; jagged chickweed (*Holosteum
umbellatum*) near Thetford and Jersey cudweed (*Gnaphalium luteoalbum*).

BRECKLAND MERES

Water in the basin-like hollows of some of the Breckland meres,
including Langmere, Ringmere, Fowlmere and the Devil's Punch-
bowl, appears and vanishes as the subterranean water table in the
underlying chalk fluctuates in level. Thus the meres may remain
more or less dry in a wet season or they may be standing half full
of water in a dry one, because of the time-lag involved while the
general level of the underground reservoir of water is adjusted.
The aquatic flora of these meres is poor and ephemeral, largely due
to the fact that the beds are more often dry than covered with water.
However, there is an interesting zonation of marsh plants in these
hollows, with lines of certain species marking the limits of flooding
reached at various periods. At the lowest level, reed canary grass
(*Phalaris arundinacea*) and amphibious bistort (*Polygonum amphibium*)
tend to maintain a perennial footing, while in summer they are
accompanied by spreading masses of water chickweed (*Myosoton

27

aquaticum). The gently sloping sides are carpeted with *Agrostis* turf, quantities of silverweed (*Potentilla anserina*), knotted pearlwort (*Sagina nodosa*) and whorled mint (*Mentha* x *verticillata*), with creeping thistle (*Cirsium arvense*), hare's-foot (*Trifolium arvense*) and sheep's fescue (*Festuca ovina*) appearing higher up until the zone of heather and bracken is reached.

Some meres, including some of those at Wretham and those formed by the damming of small watercourses, such as Thompson Water and Stanford Water, have a more usual aquatic and marginal flora, including beds of reed (*Phragmites communis*), glaucous bullrush (*Schoenoplectus tabernaemontani*), sedges (*Carex* spp.), yellow flag (*Iris pseudacorus*), purple loosestrife (*Lythrum salicaria*), hemp agrimony (*Eupatorium cannabinum*), great water dock (*Rumex hydrolapathum*), great yellow-cress (*Rorippa amphibia*), mare's-tail (*Hippuris vulgaris*) and water violet (*Hottonia palustris*). Golden dock (*Rumex maritimus*) and the hairy variety of marsh speedwell (*Veronica scutellata*) grow round some of the smaller and more pond-like meres.

From time to time, interesting stoneworts (*Charophyta*) have appeared in Fowlmere (*Chara aspera, C. contraria, Tolypella glomerata* and *Nitella flexilis*). The Wretham group of meres features the mass development of certain liverworts in some years; *Riccia cavernosa* appeared in the summers of 1921 and 1959, both drought years. The moss *Physcomitrium eurystomum*, first recorded as a British species in 1959, when it was discovered growing at the edge of Langmere, reappeared in quantity on the dried up bed of this mere in the spring of 1964.

| Scarlet flycap | Puffballs | Yellow bolet, |
| *Amanita muscaria* | *Lycoperdon perlatum* | *Boletus luteus* |

Tracts of open, stony breck are frequently found carpeted with lichens, including quantities of the brown, closely branched *Cetraria aculeata* and many kinds of cup-lichens (species of *Cladonia*). Where chalk comes close to the surface the ground is sometimes encrusted with the white lobes of *Squamarina lentigera*, bearing brown fruiting bodies which look like moon-craters. Old patches of heather are overgrown with the silvery *Parmelia saxatilis* and orange-coloured *Xanthoria parietina* and extensive cushions of *Cladonia rangiformis* often develop in the spaces where clumps of heather have died. The large grey *Peltigera canina* often flourishes on the ground of forest rides.

The agarics which appear on the heaths mainly in October are on the whole rather small and include numerous species of *Mycena*, *Leptonia* and waxy, brightly coloured *Hygrophorus*. The small golden-brown *Galerina hypnorum* is widespread. Some of the fungi present are also typical of costal dunes: these include *Omphalina pyxidata* and the large black earth-tongue, *Geoglossum cookeianum*. A bright pink parasitic fungus, *Corticium fuciforme*, is often conspicuous on the heath grasses. Yellow clustercups of the rust *Puccinia dioicae* develop on leaves of ragwort in spring and the summer spores are produced in abundance on leaves of sand sedge. Orange yellow rusts appearing on harebell, groundsel and eyebright are alternating forms of *Coleosporium tussilaginis* which has its clustercups on the needles of Scots pine. The blue anther-smut, *Schroeteria delastrina*, has been found in flowers of wall speedwell and another smut-fungus, *Ustilago violacea*, attacks anthers of the Spanish catchfly, *Silene otites*.

The mosses of bare ground and Breckland turf look at their best in early spring, especially after a wet winter. Then the yellow-green starry cushions of *Tortula ruraliformis* are very conspicuous, as are the carpets of *Polytrichum piliferum* in fertile condition. Other typical species colonizing disturbed grassy areas include *Brachythecium albicans*, *Bryum argenteum*, *Camptothecium lutescens*, *Campylium chrysophyllum*, *Dicranum scoparium*, *Eurhynchium swartzii*, *Funaria hygrometrica* (on burnt soil), *Mnium longirostrum*, *Pleurozium schreberi*, *Polytrichum juniperinum*, *Rhodobryum roseum*, *Rhytidiadelphus squarrosus* and *triquetrus*, and *Rhytidium rugosum*. In the more chalky areas the following are found: *Aloina ambigua*, *Bryum caespiticium* and *erythrocarpum*, *Climacium dendroides*, *Ctenidium molluscum*, *Ditrichum flexicaule*, *Encalypta streptocarpa*, *E. vulgaris* and *Rhacomitrium canescens*. The ubiquitous *Hypnum cupressiforme* is often plentiful on chalk and among heather. Liverworts are not conspicuous on the open brecks, but *Lophocolea cuspidata* and *Ptilidium ciliare* may be found associated with grasses in hollows where there is a certain amount of extra moisture.

| Heathland moss, | Lichen | Woodland Moss, |
| *Polytrichum juniperinum* | *Cladonia coccifera* | *Dicranum scoparium* |

EAST SUFFOLK HEATHS AND COAST, NEAR ALDEWOOD FOREST

After Thetford Chase, this is the largest of the East Anglian forest areas. Formerly, most of it consisted of open heathlands on the glacial sands and gravels flanking the rivers Blyth, Alde, Deben and Orwell. Some of the heaths are still open, though close to the afforested land; the best known of these are Hollesley Heath adjoining the Rendlesham pinewoods, Iken Heath near Tunstall and Westleton Heath near Dunwich, while farther north, Fritton Warren adjoins the Waveney plantations. Most of these areas are dominated by heather or ling (*Calluna vulgaris*), bracken (*Pteridium aquilinum*) and gorse (*Ulex europaeus*); also common locally are bell heather (*Erica cinerea*), broom (*Sarothamnus scoparius*) and the dwarf gorse (*Ulex gallii*). Characteristic plants of the open turfy ground include harebell (*Campanula rotundifolia*), heath bedstraw (*Galium saxatile*), tormentil (*Potentilla erecta*), sheep's sorrel (*Rumex acetosella*) and grasses such as sheep's fescue (*Festuca ovina*), mat-grass (*Nardus stricta*), wavy hair-grass (*Deschampsia flexuosa*) and the ephemeral *Aira praecox*. Sandy tracks across these heaths often become bright red with mossy tillaea (*Crassula tillaea*), a sort of dwarf stone-crop most frequently found in East Anglia. Hoary cinquefoil (*Potentilla argentea*) is more often seen on sandy ground in the East

Anglian Forest area than elsewhere in this country. Yellow vetch (*Vicia lutea*), believed to be indigenous on the Suffolk coast, has extended its range recently and is now found from Orford Ness to Bawdsey.

Aldewood Forest is only a few miles from the sea and so within easy reach of several estuaries and shingle beaches. Common salt-marsh plants in these areas include sea lavender (*Limonium vulgare*), sea aster (*Aster tripolium*), sea purslane (*Halimione portulacoides*) fringing the creeks, thrift (*Armeria maritima*), sea plantain (*Plantago maritima*), sea arrowgrass (*Triglochin maritima*) and sea meadow-grass (*Puccinellia maritima*). Sea beet (*Beta vulgaris* ssp. *maritima*), shore (*Atriplex littoralis*) and sea wormwood (*Artemisia maritima*) grow along the marsh walls, which are mostly topped with sea couch-grass (*Agropyron pungens*). Mudflats are largely covered in summer by marsh samphires (*Salicornia* spp.) and annual sea-blite (*Suaeda maritima*) while the rice-grass (*Spartina* x *townsendii*) has colonized and raised the level of great areas of tidal mud in recent years. The sea pea (*Lathyrus japonicus*), with its vivid green foliage and bright purple flowers, is a conspicuous feature of the beach shingle banks along the Suffolk coast; other shingle plants here include yellow horned-poppy (*Glaucium flavum*), sea campion (*Silene maritima*), curled dock (*Rumex crispus* var. *trigranulatus*), sea sandwort (*Honkenya peploides*), biting stonecrop (*Sedum acre*) and sticky groundsel (*Senecio viscosus*).

WET HEATHS AND BOGS

Because East Anglia enjoys a dry climate and is on the whole efficiently drained, few examples of country approaching moorland in character are to be found. A few such areas exist near the Commission's forests, as at Buxton Heath, Hevingham, Holt Lowes in north Norfolk, and Roydon Common, Derby, Sugar and Leziate 'fens' near King's Lynn. These lie in poorly drained valleys, usually near the sources of streams, where the soil is podzolized and where there is adjacent acid heathland. In some instances narrow strips of true fen are to be found fringing the central streams which supply base-rich water derived from chalk or boulder clay nearby. Bog plants present in one or more of these areas include cross-leaved heath (*Erica tetralix*), marsh gentian (*Gentiana pneumonanthe*), sundews (*Drosera* spp.), butterwort (*Pinguicula vulgaris*), bog asphodel (*Narthecium ossifragum*), bog pimpernel (*Anagallis tenella*), cotton-grass (*Eriophorum angustifolium*), deer-grass (*Trichophorum cespitosum*), white beak-sedge (*Rhynchospora alba*) and heath rush (*Juncus squar-rosus*). Plants growing where bog merges with fen include grass of Parnassus (*Parnassia palustris*), devil's-bit scabious (*Succisa pratensis*), louse-wort (*Pedicularis palustris*) and the bog-rush (*Schoenus nigricans*).

Scattered small areas of mixed woodland (some now felled and replanted by the Commission) occur on glacial sands and more extensively on the boulder-clays of central and south Norfolk and Suffolk. Characteristic flowering plants of the undergrowth in these woods are: wood anemone (*Anemone nemorosa*), primrose (*Primula vulgaris*), bluebell (*Endymion non-scriptus*), lesser celandine (*Ranunculus ficaria*), violets, chiefly *Viola riviniana*, wood sorrel (*Oxalis acetosella*), moschatel (*Adoxa moschatellina*), dog's mercury (*Mercurialis perennis*), red campion (*Silene dioica*), wood avens (*Geum urbanum*), enchanter's nightshade (*Circaea lutetiana*), yellow archangel (*Galeobdolon luteum*), sanicle (*Sanicula europaea*), yellow pimpernel (*Lysimachia nemorum*), St. John's worts (*Hypericum perforatum, pulchrum* and *hirsutum*), wood sage (*Teucrium scorodonia*), ramsons (*Allium ursinum*), hairy woodrush (*Luzula pilosa*), wild arum (*Arum maculatum*) and the grasses *Melica uniflora, Brachypodium sylvaticum* and *Calamagrostis epigeios*. Common woodland ferns are *Blechnum spicant, Polypodium vulgare, Athyrium filix-femina, Dryopteris filix-mas* and *D. dilatata*. The foxglove (*Digitalis purpurea*) is rare in east Norfolk, more frequent in west Norfolk and quite plentiful in parts of south Suffolk.

Rarer plants of the boulder-clay woodlands include Herb Paris (*Paris quadrifolia*), cow-wheat (*Melampyrum pratense*), greater butterfly orchid (*Platanthera chlorantha*), woodruff (*Galium odoratum*) and lily of the valley (*Convallaria majalis*). The May lily (*Maianthemum bifolium*) grows in only one wood, close to a forestry plantation in north Norfolk, and the creeping lady's tresses (*Goodyera repens*), possibly introduced with pines from Scotland in the nineteenth century, is established in the neighbourhood of Holt. The true oxlip (*Primula elatior*) which has a peculiarly East Anglian distribution in this country, abounds in woods on clay in south Suffolk. Where woodlands are felled and brushwood is burned, the cleared areas are colonized by rose-bay willow-herb (*Epilobium angustifolium*) and wood groundsel (*Senecio sylvaticus*). Perfoliate purslane (*Montia perfoliata*) is locally abundant in pine woods on light soils.

Except very locally in river valleys and near the sea, lichens are not prominent on trees in this region and call for no special mention in this survey. Similarly, there is nothing very remarkable about the woodland mosses, which receive little encouragement from the dry climate. Extensive cushions of *Mnium hornum* cover woodland floors and banks, with *Dicranella heteromalla* spreading like yellow-green velvet in some of the drier places in spring. *Brachythecium rutabulum* is the most abundant moss, growing on the ground and on

fallen boughs in boulder-clay woods, where it is commonly associated with *Eurhynchium praelongum*, while *Hypnum cupressiforme*
grows some way up the bases of living tree trunks. The gold-green,
fern-like *Thuidium tamariscinum* flourishes in the damper woodland
rides, while the ball-like whitish cushion-moss *Leucobryum glaucum*
is sometimes common on the leaf-mould of beech-woods. The woods
of East Anglia produce toadstools in great variety in rainy seasons.
The notorious death-cap (*Amanita phalloides*) is commoner here
than in any other part of Britain and is usually associated with oak
woods. The quaint earth-stars (*Geastrum* spp.) grow here in greater
abundance and variety than elsewhere, especially on the glacial
sands. With the introduction of a large proportion of conifers in
the new forests, the destructive pine fungus *Fomes annosus* has shown
a corresponding increase, as have several of the agarics and boleti
specially associated with conifers.

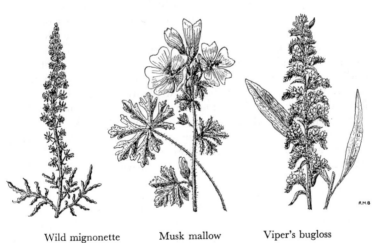

Wild mignonette   Musk mallow   Viper's bugloss

Golden pheasant

ANIMAL LIFE

BY RUTH M. RACE

MAMMALS

Hedgehogs are common in all districts, living in hedgebanks, woods and gardens. They may be met with in the heart of Breckland's conifer forests, feeding at night on slugs and beetles along the grassy woodland rides. All three of our native shrews occur; both the common and pygmy shrews live in the undergrowth of woodlands as well as in grassland and heather on the brecks and coastal heaths. Water-shrews, although most plentiful in the Broads area, also live along the rivers and streams farther inland, and are occasionally recorded in south and south-west Norfolk.

Moles are very plentiful on the sandy soils of Breckland, where colour variation is not uncommon and animals with pale grey, golden orange, light brown, cream or off-white fur are sometimes reported.

Although naturalists in East Anglia have been making organised studies of bats during the last few years, these animals are still not very well known in the region. The pipistrelle is known to be common throughout the area, where large colonies breed in many churches and old houses. The noctule is plentiful in some localities and may be seen catching cockchafers over woods at sunset in late spring. The long-eared bat is found chiefly in well wooded areas; Daubenton's and Natterer's are probably fairly common and the barbastelle is recorded occasionally. Whiskered bats have been found roosting in the prehistoric flint-mines at Grime's Graves, from where bones of several other bats, including Bechstein's, have been discovered by excavation. The lesser horseshoe bat has been

34

recorded from Suffolk, near Bury St. Edmunds. The serotine lives in several localities in East Suffolk and has been found recently on the Norfolk side of the Waveney Valley.

Much of Breckland was covered by rabbit warrens up to the time forestry planting commenced and the character of the vegetation was greatly modified by the grazing of vast numbers of these rodents. Myxomatosis killed off most of the rabbits in 1954–55 and the disease breaks out periodically, but numbers have now increased again, despite the activities of rabbit-clearance societies. Black rabbits used to be common on the brecks and they are now reappearing, and several white ones have been seen recently.

Hares are very plentiful in the Breck and other open areas of sandy country and arable land. The population rose very noticeably during the years 1954–59, following the decline in rabbits due to myxomatosis, but it then slightly declined. Many of these animals have been coming to feed in woodlands recently and it has been suggested that they do this because some of the chemical sprays used on field crops and grasslands are distasteful to them.

Bank- and field-voles and the long-tailed field-mouse abound throughout the region, the field mouse living chiefly in mixed woods and on forest margins. Field-voles in some years become very numerous in grassland on the brecks and elsewhere. The yellow-necked field-mouse, which has an orange-coloured band across the chest, flourishes in many woods in Suffolk, but appears to be virtually absent from Norfolk. Water-voles are present along most rivers and streams and dark brown and black forms are specially prevalent in north Norfolk and round the Broads. Dormice have become extinct in Norfolk, but some are still to be found farther south, in the Stour valley. Harvest-mice used to breed in cornfields throughout the region until modern agricultural methods of crop treatment and harvesting discouraged them; they are still common locally in rough marshes and reed beds, which are their natural haunts.

Red squirrels are widely distributed and generally plentiful throughout the forest areas of Norfolk and Suffolk and specially so in conifer plantations, where nibbled pine cones on the ground show where they have been at work. North American grey squirrels have been very slow in reaching East Anglia, in comparison with other parts of England. Some invaded south and south-west Suffolk between 1955 and 1960 and the population has since rapidly increased. They have now reached Norfolk, particularly the Breckland area, in some numbers.

The introduced coypu, a cat-sized, amphibious South American rodent, became established along the waterways in east Norfolk following escapes from a fur farm near Norwich in 1937. Coloniza-

RMB

Pine cone frayed by crossbill   Pine cone stripped by red squirrel

tion of marshes extended to west Norfolk and the coastal area of Suffolk in the 1950's and after the population had reached pest proportions official measures were taken to check any further spread and to eliminate coypus gradually from the outer fringe of penetration to the centre of dispersal. The campaign was helped by the severe winter of 1963 but isolated populations have built up again, including several groups around the Breckland meres.

Foxes are found scattered throughout the region and there has been a marked increase in their numbers in recent years. Badgers are fairly rare in Norfolk, but slightly less so in Suffolk. They have shown a great readiness to colonize Commission plantations in suitable parts of Breckland. Otters inhabit many streams and rivers in the area, but are nowhere plentiful and seldom met with. Some are present at Stanford and Thompson Waters and in the Little Ouse valley. Stoats are usually plentiful when rabbits abound, although numbers decreased for a time following myxomatosis. In Breckland, owing to the locally more extreme winter climate, it used to be commoner for these animals to turn partly white or assume full ermine dress than elsewhere in East Anglia. Weasels, which prey on small mammals, are common throughout the region and were not affected when myxomatosis killed off most of the rabbits. Polecats and pine-martens formerly inhabited this part of the country, but are now extinct here. It is possible that both species might return eventually to live in the new forests, although it seems rather more probable that mink escaping from fur farms may become established sooner.

Red and roe deer were formerly indigenous to East Anglia, but hunting and deforestation led to their extermination in historical times. In recent years, park deer have escaped from time to time, and red deer have become established in the Breckland forests, some of the heads of stags there being among the finest in Britain. Fallow deer are also present.

Several pairs of roe were brought over from Germany and released near Downham High Lodge in 1884. They spread southward into Suffolk and across the Little Ouse into Norfolk and became fairly numerous in Breckland. Their numbers fell during widespread fellings between 1914 and 1922, but thereafter fresh cover was provided in the Commission's plantations. With the

Crossbill

37

growth of the forests these small deer have become well established. Muntjac deer, mainly the Chinese species which was introduced at Woburn early this century, are now found in many counties and their occurrence is fairly frequently reported in East Anglia.

BIRDS

Afforestation has done much to change the character of bird-life in Breckland. There has been a great increase in the population of titmice, thrushes, blackbirds, woodpeckers and other arboreal species. The change has favoured the breeding of lesser redpolls, while crossbills, long associated with the older pine belts, have not yet shown any great inclination to multiply in the new plantations, although they may do so as the pine forests become more mature. The presence of crossbills can be detected by the characteristically frayed cones found on the ground under trees where the birds have been feeding; but the birds themselves are very elusive and keep largely to the treetops, where they build their nests in winter, earlier than any other species.

In the denser parts of the older plantations birds are few; there is an impressive silence as one walks through the dim aisles; even when wood pigeons are disturbed, they fly away noiselessly. Sometimes one hears the high-pitched squeaking notes of goldcrests in the tops of tall trees, and the call-notes of various titmice travelling about the forests in family parties.

Chaffinches penetrate the denser parts of the forest, and the harsh cries of jays and magpies are sometimes heard there. Mistle thrushes are quite common and may often be seen flying along the open rides in a series of long swoops. The hobby, which is only an occasional visitor to the rest of East Anglia, may still linger as a breeding species in the Breckland forests, where long-eared owls still nest every year, though in small numbers.

Birds living in the wooded areas, often far from the nearest watercourse, commonly drink from the static water tanks provided for forestry purposes. Among the species which can be seen at the tanks are various finches, yellowhammers, linnets, willow-warblers, tree sparrows, jays, woodpeckers and turtle doves.

Redstarts and red-backed shrikes inhabit the forest edges and adjoining open heathland, where also a good many nightjars can be met with from mid-May to August, uttering their weird churring notes at dusk and dawn. Birds typical of the open brecks have all become scarcer in recent years; they include wheatears which used to breed in rabbit burrows, stonechat, whinchat and woodlark. Redshank and ringed plover used to nest in considerable numbers on the sandy warrens round about Thetford but now only a very few pairs breed there. Other open breck species have adapted themselves to the changing conditions: the stone curlew now nests freely in forest rides, especially those ploughed regularly as firebreaks, also in young plantations and in ploughed fields. The common curlew has made its appearance as a breeding bird in the Breck in recent years and is now well established in both Norfolk and Suffolk, nesting in open areas between forest compartments and on some of the still sandy warrens. Woodcock find some of the new plantations attractive as nesting sites.

Introduced game birds thrive in Breckland and these include a large number of feral golden pheasants, which have become established over a wide area. A recent colonist, by its own efforts, is the collared dove.

Breckland was the last home of indigenous great bustards in England. Some 200 to 300 years ago, before the planting of fir belts, they roamed in flocks over the far-flung sandy warrens. They became exterminated round about 1839. An attempt was made to re-introduce them at Elvedon in 1900, but the experiment proved unsuccessful. Now the great bustard is only a very rare and erratic visitor to this country.

The Breckland meres attract numerous water-birds. Great crested grebes nest on some of them and they provide the main breeding centre for one species of duck in East Anglia—the gadwall. Visitors include most kinds of wild duck in season, including many goosanders in winter, when Bewick's swans also arrive and stay for long periods. Gulls and terns also come to the meres, the latter often calling as they are travelling overland on passage migration. Waders which drop in from time to time include common and green sandpipers, greenshank and ruffs.

East Suffolk Coastal Marshes

The famous nature reserves of Minsmere and Havergate Island lie close to the Commission plantations around Dunwich, Tunstall and Rendlesham. At Minsmere rare breeding birds include bearded tit, bittern and marsh harrier. Avocets returned to nest at Havergate first in 1948 and a spectacular colony of these long-legged, black-and-white waders with upturned bills has become established there, under the care of the Royal Society for the Protection of Birds. Shelduck abound on this coastal strip and many nest in dunes and nearby heathland. The little ringed plover has bred at Minsmere and in gravel workings on the Suffolk coast. Winter visitors to the marshes include the hen-harrier and rough-legged buzzard, while twites, snow buntings and shorelarks feed in grassy areas near the beaches.

39

In the scattered woodlands of the country, stretching from west Norfolk across to the Cromer-Holt area, with others about North Walsham and Hevingham, a wide selection of sylvan birds may be found. The delightful little wood warbler calls for special mention as a nesting species in this area. Occasional visitors include common, rough-legged and honey buzzards and the red kite has appeared a few times in recent years. This is a great 'catchment' area for incoming autumn migrants, including flocks of fieldfares and redwings and sometimes a good many waxwings. Some of the largest winter roosts of starlings are situated here.

REPTILES AND AMPHIBIANS

Adders and common lizards are fairly common on sandy heathlands bordering the forests in all parts of the region except in the boulder-clay country. Grass-snakes thrive chiefly near marshes and rivers which they visit in summer in search of tadpoles and small fishes.

Frogs, toads and slow-worms may be found in all districts, although they are becoming generally scarcer, possibly as a result of the use of certain agricultural chemicals and because a great many are killed on the roads nowadays. Natterjack toads are quite numerous in a few coastal areas where they spawn in ditches and shallow pools near the sand dunes and utter their rattling 'songs' in late spring and summer. Edible frogs have been introduced into Norfolk from France and Belgium at various times from 1837 onward and have persisted for varying periods. Most appear to have died out, including those released near Thetford in 1939, but happily one very old established colony is still thriving.

FISHES

The rivers of this region are well stocked with coarse fish, notably pike, perch, roach, rudd and bream. The faster-flowing upper reaches are inhabited by dace, gudgeon, stone loach, ruffe, bullhead and minnow. Brown trout, rainbow trout, and grayling have been introduced. The chub is indigenous in west Norfolk rivers (Ouse, Wissey and Thet) but not in those flowing eastward. Tench abound in many lakes and some of the Breckland meres. The migratory lampern and smelt come upstream from the sea to spawn in spring. The spotted burbot used to be found in some of the Breckland rivers but has not been found recently.

INSECTS

Two kinds of moths are found only in Breckland in this country. These are the Viper's Bugloss Moth, whose caterpillars feed on the

Plate 21. Norfolk windmill

Plate 22.
(Above).
Young pine-
woods seen
from a fire
look-out
tower.

Plate 23.
(Left). Aerial
view of pine
plantations
near
Brandon.
D5229

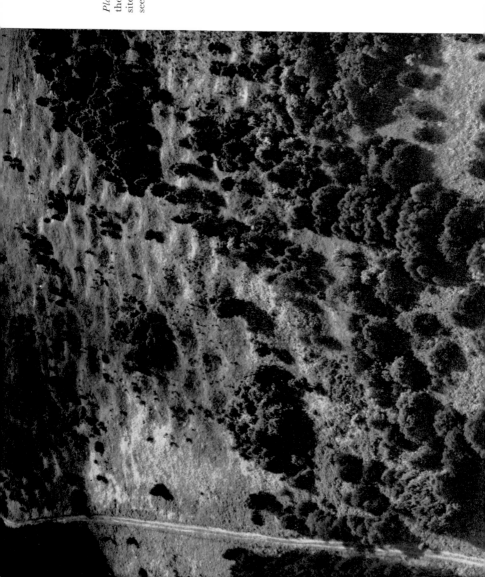

Plate 24. Grime's Graves, the Neolithic flint mine site north of Brandon, seen from the air. HC 89

Plate 25. Bittern and young at their nest in the reedbeds

Plate 26. Dormouse

Plate 27. Noctule bat

Plate 28. Brown hare

Plate 29. Rabbit in snow

Plate 30. Red squirrel

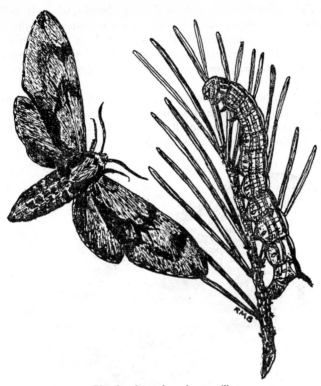

Pine hawk moth and caterpillar

Spanish catchfly, and the Grey Carpet, whose food plants are treacle mustard and flixweed. Three further species are almost wholly confined to that area: the Spotted Sulphur, with larvae on bindweed, the Tawny Wave, feeding on trefoils, and a Pyralid, the Diamond-spot Pearl, feeding on mugwort. Other Breckland specialities include two Tineid moths, *Monopis imella* and *Gelechia vilella* and a plume moth, *Oxyptilus distans*. The uncommon Palelemon Sallow is well established in the Mildenhall district, where the larvae feed on buds and catkins of poplar in spring. The Barberry Carpet breeds on barberry in hedges. The Marbled Clover is more frequently seen in East Anglia, especially on the brecks, than elsewhere. The Small Elephant Hawk moth and the Cream-spot Tiger occur in the Breck district and other less common moths include the Maple Prominent and Bordered Sallow. Several mainly coastal moths occur also in the sandy brecks; these include the Archer's Dart, the Oblique-striped and the White

Colon. The Cinnabar abounds on the grass heaths, where its yellow-and-black caterpillars destroy ragwort on a vast scale; this conspicuous crimson-and-black moth is very much at the mercy of the wind when it flutters off the ground and it depends on random dispersal in this way for reaching new colonies of ragwort from year to year.

Typical butterflies of the brecks, heaths and coast sands are the Meadow Brown, Hedge Brown, Ringlet, Small Heath, Small Copper, Grayling, Wall, Small Skipper and Common Blue. The Silver-studded Blue and Essex Skipper appear more locally.

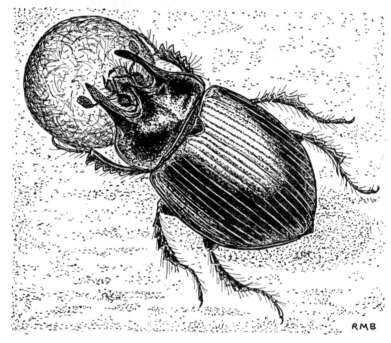

Trident beetle, *Typhaeus typhaeus*, with rabbit dropping.

The Trident-beetle (*Typhaeus typhaeus*) is locally abundant on sandy ground, where it buries rabbit-droppings as food for its larvae. The rarer scarabaeid *Copris lunaris*, which makes balls of cow-dung for its grubs, has been found in Breckland. Tiger beetles run and fly over the heaths in many places in summer. The metallic Chrysomelid beetle *Sermylassa halensis*, most commonly a coast insect, flourishes inland on lady's bedstraw on many of the open brecks.

Many kinds of solitary bees, digger wasps and sand wasps

flourish in the sandy areas, which are convenient for burrowing. Some of the robber flies found typically on dunes also appear on the brecks, where another seaside insect, the Marram Bug (*Chorosoma schillingi*) has been found living on grasses. Short-horned grasshoppers of five species, including the coastal *Chorthippus albomarginatus* are conspicuously common.

The larger breck meres have a rich freshwater fauna of dragon-flies, water-boatmen and aquatic beetles, but the meres which dry out periodically have fewer species which, however, may reach abundance individually at times. Caterpillars of the Eyed Hawk Moth occur on sallow bushes round some of the meres; there also one may find the red-and-black froghopper, *Cercopis vulnerata*, otherwise uncommon in East Anglia. The European Chinch Bug, first noticed in Breckland in 1956, on barley, is now well established on grasses round the meres and in the river valleys.

Many insects are associated specially with conifer plantations and with scattered pines. They include the Pine Hawk Moth, whose caterpillars are well camouflaged as they feed on pine needles; other moths with larvae feeding on the needles are the Bordered White, Pine Beauty, Pine Carpet and Grey Pine Carpet. The Pine Shoot Moth damages the leading shoots of pines in young plantations and causes some trees to grow in curious curves, like post-horns. In 1960 a small Tortricid moth, the Beautiful Twist, was noticed on Breckland pines for the first time; this species, first recorded in Britain in 1945, may be expected to increase here in years to come.

Butterflies of the Suffolk woods include the Purple Emperor, White Admiral, High Brown and Silver-washed Fritillaries and the Purple and White-letter Hairstreaks. The Speckled Wood has been spreading recently in Norfolk, both in the northern area and in Breckland, but not in Suffolk.

Many rare bugs and beetles have been found in the Breckland forests, where various bark beetles, longhorns and the pine weevil occur in great abundance, as do the conifer gall-lice (*Adelges* spp.) which deposit white fluffy material as a cover for their eggs on fir and pine shoots. Two pine sawflies are pests in the forests: *Diprion pini*, with yellowish green caterpillar-like larvae ornamented with a line of black dots along the back, and *Neodiprion sertifer*, whose larvae are dark grey-green and marked with light and dark longitudinal stripes. Stems of conifers are occasionally tunnelled by the wood-wasps *Urocerus gigas* (yellow and brown) and *Sirex juvencus* (metallic blue). Their ichneumon parasite, *Rhyssa persuasoria*, a slender black-and-yellow spotted insect with very long wire-like tail appendages used for boring and egg-laying, is found with them.

A great many moths of special interest are associated with coast

Tiger beetle, *Cicindela campestris*

and salt-marsh vegetation along the Suffolk seaboard; they include a very fine series of the Wainscot moths which feed on grasses, and the Starwort Shark which breeds abundantly on sea aster.

Finally, it should be mentioned that a number of interesting spiders have been discovered recently on the brecks and East Suffolk heaths; many of these appear to be restricted to this region in Britain, where they find local conditions closely resembling those of arid steppes and Continental heathlands.

BIBLIOGRAPHY

British Association for the Advancement of Science, Briers, F. (ed.) *Norwich and its Region*, 1961.

Clarke, W. G. *In Breckland Wilds*, 1925, revised by R. R. Clarke 1937.
Payn, W. H. *The Birds of Suffolk*, 1962.
Petch, C. P., and Swann, E. L. West Norfolk Plants Today, 1962: Supplement to
   Proc. Bot. Soc. Brit. Is., 4, part 4.
Petch, C. P. and Swann, E. L. *Flora of Norfolk*, 1968.
Riviere, B. B. *A History of the Birds of Norfolk*, 1930.
Seago, M. J. *Birds of Norfolk*, 1967.
General—*Transactions of the Norfolk and Norwich Naturalists' Society.*
   Transactions of the Suffolk Naturalists' Society.

On Bridgham Heath, near Thetford

TOPOGRAPHY, GEOLOGY AND SOILS

BY R. M. S. PERRIN

TOPOGRAPHY

East Anglia consists essentially of a low plateau which reaches a maximum height of 420 feet above sea level near Depden in West Suffolk.

This plateau is bounded on the north-west and west by the Wash and the Fen Basins, some of which lie at or below sea level: to the south-west it merges into the extension of the Chilterns in South Cambridgeshire. To the east it slopes gently away to Broadland, all of which lies at less than 25 feet above sea level, and to the Suffolk heaths which rarely rise above 80 feet. It is breached from east to west in the Breckland by the through valley linking the Little Ouse with the River Waveney.

A conspicuous feature in north Norfolk is the Cromer Ridge; this extends from Holt to the coast at Mundesley, and attains a maximum height of 327 feet (Plate 13).

The main watershed runs, in general terms, from just to the east of Hunstanton south south-east to a point about four miles west of Diss. Thence it trends south south-west passing about five miles south of Bury St. Edmunds, and then west south-west towards Saffron Walden. To the west of this line the main rivers are the Cam, Lark, Little Ouse, Wissey and Nar which flow into the Great Ouse, all drainage in this area ultimately going north to Kings

46

Lynn to enter the Wash. To the east the drainage is carried by the rivers Chelmer, Colne, Stour, Gipping, Deben, Waveney, Yare, Wensum and Bure which run to the North Sea between Burnham and Yarmouth on the east cost. The Cromer ridge forms a subsidiary watershed in the extreme north of the area, but only a few minor streams such as the Glaven reach the sea on the North Norfolk coast. (See Drift map, p. 53, for river-valley alluvium).

The physiography of the area is discussed in more detail in Briers (1961), Chatwin (1954) and Steers (1942).

GEOLOGY AND SOILS

In English terminology *solid* formation are those dating from before the onset of the Pleistocene (or 'Ice Age') glaciations referred to on p. 53. *Drift*, or *superficial*, deposits are those produced by the glaciations themselves, mainly consisting of till or boulder clay and associated glacial sands and gravels, and those laid down in Post-glacial (Holocene or Recent) times which include alluvium, coastal deposits, blown sand and peat. The geology of the district is discussed in more detail in Briers (1961), Chatwin (1954) and Larwood and Funnell (1961).

Due to the extensive glaciation of the area, none of the land surfaces are very old and some are extremely young. The pattern of soils is thus determined mainly by differences in surface geology and local topography. It will therefore be most convenient to consider the soils associated with each geological formation as it is described. The main features of the soil types found in East Anglia are briefly described in the appendix (p. 59). Space does not permit description of the processes of soil-formation that have been operative but short accounts will be found in Briers (1961) and in Hey and Perrin (1960).

SOLID FORMATIONS

(See geological map, key, and geological section, pp. 48–50.)
Palaeozoic Floor

The basement of old hard rocks is in the form of a low ridge running east north-east—west south-west. It underlies the area at depths which vary from 360 feet below sea level at Cambridge to 1,013 feet below at Harwich, and to 1,615 feet below at Lowestoft.

Resting on this floor are Mesozoic rocks of the Jurassic and Cretaceous Systems. The former are unimportant for our present purposes: they outcrop only in the Fenland on the western margin of East Anglia and thin out and disappear eastwards where the Cretaceous rests directly on the Palaeozoic formations.

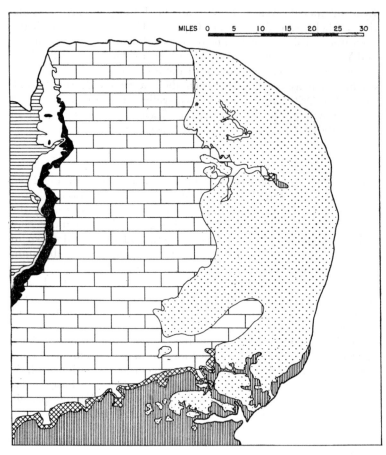

Geological map: Solid geology

Neocomian and Lower Greensand

The oldest beds which we need consider are those outcropping in north-west Norfolk. The Neocomian is represented by the Sandringham Sands, mainly light-coloured sands, locally glauconitic or cemented with iron oxide, which were laid down in a shallow sea. The Lower Greensand consists of the Snettisham Clay, which is of little importance, and the Carstone. The latter consists of sands and ferruginous sandstone, of a warm gingerbread colour, which gives its name to the formation; it has been much used locally as a building stone. These mainly permeable, and therefore relatively resistant deposits give rise to a low escarpment fronting

48

the Fens which is well seen near Downham Market and which passes into low cliffs at Heacham.

Drift is relatively thin over much of this area and the local sands and sandstones are the parent materials of most of the soils. Due to high permeability and ready leaching, these are generally podzolic brown earths or humus podzols with gley podzols in low-lying ill-drained sites.

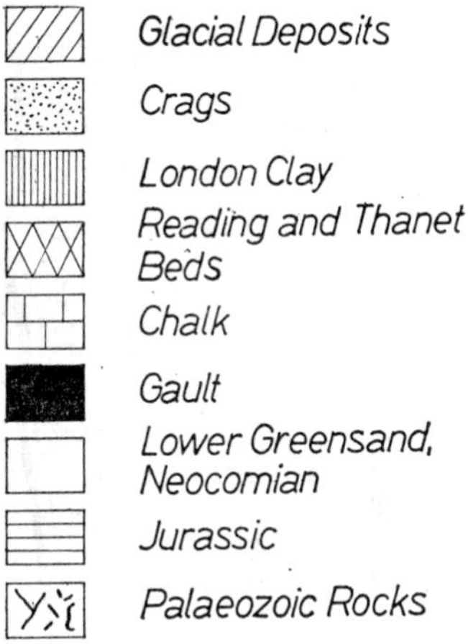

Glacial Deposits

Crags

London Clay

Reading and Thanet Beds

Chalk

Gault

Lower Greensand, Neocomian

Jurassic

Palaeozoic Rocks

Key to geological map

Gault

Overlying the Greensand is the Gault, consisting in north-west Norfolk of marly clay which passes northwards into a reddish limestone, the Red Rock of the Hunstanton cliffs. Due to its generally impermeable character, it has been eroded down to low levels and has been covered with drift. It thus has little influence on local scenery or soils apart from locally causing some impedance and gleying in the latter.

Chalk

The chalk is by far the most important solid formation. As will be seen from the Section it underlies the whole area except for the narrow outcrops of the Neocomian, Lower Greensand and Gault, but it dips gently eastwards and is there covered with Tertiary and Quaternary deposits.

Following the deposition of the Gault, slow sinking of the Palaeo-

49

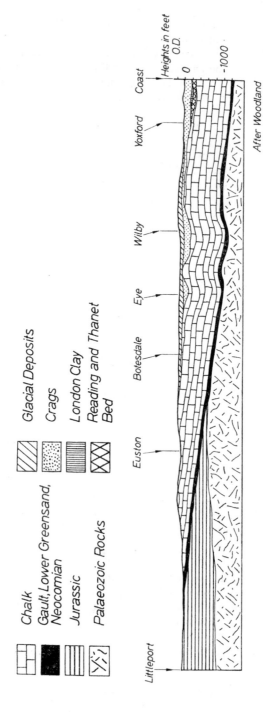

Geological section from Littleport, near Ely south-east by east, towards the Suffolk coast near Leiston

Chalk

Gault, Lower Greensand, Neocomian

Jurassic

Palaeozoic Rocks

Glacial Deposits

Crags

London Clay

Reading and Thanet Bed

Littleport

Euston

Botesdale

Eye

Wilby

Yoxford

Coast

Heights in feet O.D.

0

-1000

After Woodland

zoic floor gave rise to a shallow but very extensive sea in which there accumulated vast quantities of ooze, mainly composed of the remains of calcareous algae together with foraminifera and shell fragments. In the early stages the sea contained more terrigenous mud, and the Lower Chalk thus often contains substantial amounts of non-calcareous material. The Middle, and especially the Upper, Chalks are much purer and may contain 99 per cent of calcium carbonate. Flints occur mainly in the Upper Chalk and are believed to originate from silica derived from sponge spicules in the original ooze. Under parts of Norfolk the thickness of the Chalk is 1,200 feet.

Earth movements at the close of the Cretaceous Period raised the Chalk above sea level and initiated sub-aerial erosion. It was also subjected to gentle tilting and folding, the main dip being imparted in Miocene times. This dip is not uniform: in south-west Suffolk and south Cambridgeshire it is south-east, in north Suffolk it is east while north of the Wissey it is east north-east, its magnitude being about 1° or less.

In the east of the area the Chalk surface has been covered by Tertiary deposits (see page 52) but elsewhere it has been subjected to long periods of erosion and thus thins out to the west. In general it forms a low plateau intersected by valleys. There are slight escarpments round Newmarket and in north-west Norfolk. Between these two areas in the Breckland there is no escarpment, and the plateau is breached by the Ouse-Waveney valley, the Chalk surface sloping imperceptibly down to the Fens.

In two shallow valleys in the area are found the Breckland meres; the Devil's Punch Bowl, Fowlmere (Plate 17), Home Mere, Mickle Mere and the Wretham Park meres in one, and Langmere and Ringmere in the other. These are shallow ponds, probably formed by solution of the Chalk in Post-glacial time, in which the water level fluctuates with that in the underlying Chalk; at times of low level the ponds dry up completely.

Although much of the Chalk has been subjected to weathering for very long periods, there are no areas where the soils are purely derived from its insoluble residue. Any soils formed in Tertiary times were removed by glaciation (see p. 53), and everywhere there are deposits of drift. In some areas these are very thick but even where they are too thin to have been mapped they are sufficient to swamp the very small amount of residue from the Chalk. In these areas of thin drift, however, the Chalk has had a profound effect on soil-formation. Because of its high permeability it allows ready percolation, and thus leaching, except in very low-lying sites. Secondly, the thin drifts over Chalk were often highly calcareous initially. The development of soils on such drifts is described on p. 54.

The scenery of the country underlain by the Chalk is variable according to the nature and thickness of the drift. (Plate 20). Round Newmarket, where the drift is thin, there is an area of downland with shallow brown calcareous soils carrying a short turf and few trees. Similar conditions prevail south-east of Hunstanton. Elsewhere the superficial deposits have greater influence as discussed below.

Tertiary and Early Pleistocene

Following the period of emergence and erosion of the Chalk referred to above, part of the area was again inundated by the sea in Eocene times. The earliest of these deposits are the shallow-water sands and clays of the Thanet Beds and the Reading Beds. They outcrop mainly between Sudbury and Ipswich but are thickly covered with drift and are thus unimportant.

In north-east Essex the late Eocene is represented by the London Clay. This formation, consisting of grey and brown clays, outcrops over extensive tracts, and where it is drift-free, or has been much incorporated in the local drift, it gives rise to surface-water gleys of extremely heavy texture which probably originally developed under dense mixed oak forest.

During the Oligocene and Miocene our area is thought to have stood above sea level and there are no deposits referable to these divisions. The latest important solid formations are the Crags and the Pebbly Gravels, or Westleton Beds, of the Pliocene and early Pleistocene. The Crags are mainly shelly sands laid down in shallow seas: the earliest, the Coralline Crag, was deposited in warm conditions at the end of the Pliocene but the later Crags show evidence of increasingly cold conditions marking the onset of the Pleistocene.

These deposits underlie considerable areas of East Norfolk and Suffolk but they are largely covered by later drift. In East Norfolk they outcrop along the major valleys in the area of the Norwich Brickearth (see p. 54). The soils on the valley sides are usually derived from mixed parent materials and are mainly brown earths with a rather coarse texture.

The Crags and Westleton Beds also outcrop locally in East Suffolk. Where they form the surface these light-textured parent materials give rise to podzolic brown earths and humus podzols. Most of this region, however, is covered by glacial sands and gravels and in most cases it is these drifts which are the parent materials of the soils.

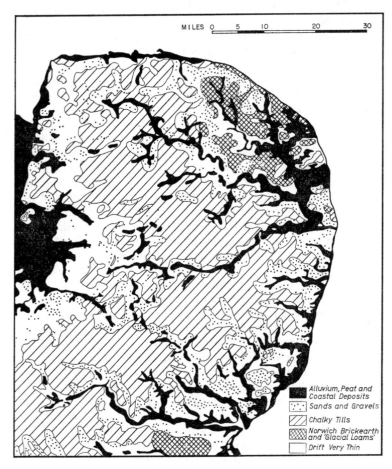

Drift map

DRIFT FORMATIONS (see Drift map)

It appears that three glaciations have affected East Anglia:
these are now usually referred to as the Lowestoft. Gipping and
Hunstanton Glaciations.

Lowestoft Glaciation

In this glaciation there is evidence of two advances. The *Cromer
Advance* brought ice moving south-eastwards across north-east
Norfolk. It deposited the Cromer Till on the coast and also the
Norwich Brickearth, which covers extensive tracts inland. Both

these tills contain materials brought across what is now the floor of the North Sea.

The Cromer Till is everywhere covered by later drift but the surface of the Norwich Brickearth is relatively free and is deeply weathered. On it have been formed brown earths under deciduous forest which have long been exploited as valuable arable soils. In low-lying sites, or locally where the till is heavier in texture, brown earths with gleying are found.

During the *Lowestoft Advance*, ice passed over the rest of East Anglia moving essentially from the west. In North Norfolk the Lowestoft Till is an extremely chalky grey clay; in south Norfolk and in Suffolk it is a heavy blue-grey clay mainly derived from the Jurassic clays with chalk pebbles and erratics from the Midlands and north of England. At the end of the Lowestoft Advance it is probable that most of the pre-existing topography of East Anglia was submerged beneath Lowestoft Till or its outwash. There followed a long mild period, the Hoxnian Interglacial, in which the till was weathered and dissected; it was almost entirely removed from the major valleys, some of which were excavated down to the underlying Chalk, but survived as extensive plateaux on the main interfluves. These caps of Lowestoft Till have, however, been covered by deposits of later drifts, and although these are often so thin that the till strongly influences the nature of the soil, the latter is rarely exclusively derived from it.

In the ensuing *Gipping Glaciation* ice again advanced into East Anglia but this time from a more northerly direction across north-west Norfolk down into Suffolk. In north-east Norfolk it advanced only as far south as the Cromer-Holt ridge, and the coarse sandy and gravelly deposits of this area represent accumulations of outwash from the Gipping ice, although the manner of deposition was complex. The Gipping ice probably did not penetrate into south-east Norfolk or north-east Suffolk at any time.

On the chalk in north-west Norfolk, and in Breckland, the Gipping Till is locally very chalky. Leaching out of chalk has produced a well marked development sequence of soils: immature calcareous soil—rendzina—brown calcareous soil—brown earth. The time available for soil formation has normally sufficed for the early stages in this sequence to have been passed, and the immature soils and rendzinas are thus found only as a result of erosion on slopes or of human interference. In the last stages of decalcification, fine clay seems to become mobile and a sticky reddish brown coloured textural B horizon has often formed. Where the till is exceptionally sandy, or where clay migration has left an impoverished A horizon, podzolic brown earths or even humus podzols occur. These very light topsoils may be readily eroded and re-distributed by wind. Soil-formation may then recommence on stabilized sand dunes. All these stages may be observed in the Breckland, together with the corresponding gleyed soils in low-lying areas.

In the high-lying plateau areas of mid-Norfolk and mid-Suffolk, Gipping ice passed over the remnants of the Lowestoft Till with progressive incorporation of its debris. On the lighter parent materials in the north one therefore finds brown earths, and brown earths with gleying, while in south Norfolk, and especially in mid-Suffolk, surface-water gleys become much more prominent, although the drainage conditions in the topsoils have been much improved by artificial means in the last two hundred years.

Outwash Deposits

As soil parent materials the outwash sands and gravels of any of the glaciations are similar to the light-textured phases of the Gipping Till. Where, as is usually the case, the outwash is non-calcareous, it has given rise to brown earths of low base status, podzolic brown earths and humus podzols. These are specially characteristic of the Cromer Ridge and some of the outwash areas between it and Norwich, and of the east Suffolk heaths. In the western part of our area outwash deposits tend to be more calcareous: here brown earths of rather higher base status, and occasionally brown calcareous soils, are more evident.

The Hunstanton Glaciation

The Gipping Glaciation was followed by the Ipswichian Inter-glacial, in which soil formation commenced on Gipping materials. This process was interrupted by the last or Hunstanton Glaciation in which a brown till was deposited along the north Norfolk coast between Hunstanton and Morston, but probably nowhere else. However, periglacial conditions prevailed in the rest of East Anglia at this time and led to frost-heaving and solifluxion, evidence of which is preserved at the present time as contortions in soil profiles and as surface patterns in soils, natural vegetation or crops, which can readily be identified on air photographs (Plate 16). In spite of this disturbance, the essential pattern of soil parent materials established in the upland areas at the end of the Gipping Glaciation was not greatly altered.

Post-glacial Deposits

The terms Holocene or Recent are often used for Post-glacial deposits. There is however a growing tendency to regard Post-glacial time as part of the Pleistocene. Both forms of usage are shown in the table on p. 58.

Fenland (see Plate 18)

The Fens on the western margin of our area occupy a large basin in soft Jurassic and Cretaceous sediments which already existed at the close of the Pleistocene. Accompanying the general rise in sea level due to the melting of ice sheets in Post-glacial times, this basin has filled with the so-called Fen Deposits. These consist on the one hand of basin peats laid down in ponded-back fresh water and on the other of estuarine silt and clay. The two types of deposit alternate, but the beds in which they occur are wedge-shaped, those of peat becoming thinner towards the sea, those of silt and clay becoming thinner towards the land. Artificial drainage in historical times has produced two extremely valuable agricultural areas: to the north are the pinkish-brown coloured brown warp soils derived from the Fen Silts, while to the south are the black basin peats and dark grey peaty gleys derived from the Fen Peats with more or less admixture of mineral matter ploughed up from below.

Broadland

Similar processes on a smaller scale led to the infilling of the estuary system now known as Broadland. Here peat beds formed in the upper reaches while estuarine muds were deposited nearer to the sea. Recent work has shown that many of the Broads result from flooding of extensive peat diggings dating from Mediaeval times (see Plate 19).

Coastal Areas

The relative rise of sea-level has led to the drowning and partial infilling of other river valleys in the area, for example those of the Alde, Deben, Orwell and Stour. It has also favoured the rapid erosion of the soft, mainly Pleistocene, sediments of which the coast is composed. Such erosion has been especially severe between Happisburgh and Yarmouth and around Dunwich and Eccles. Much of the debris has, however, been carried along the coast by longshore waves and currents and redeposited either as muds, as in the Wash or the north Norfolk marshes, or as spits of shingle and associated blown sand, as at Scolt Head, Blakeney and Orford Ness.

In the higher parts of the muds stabilized under salt-marsh vegetation there are developed marsh gleys. To the north, the

Plate 31. Fox cub

Plate 32. Hedgehog

Plate 33. Shelduck

Plate 34. (Above). Otter

Plate 35. (Below). Coypu

Plate 36. Yellowhammer and nestlings

Plate 37. Stone curlew and eggs

Plate 38. Nightingale

Plate 39. Long-tailed tit, nest and nestlings

Plate 40. Nightjar at rest

Plate 41. Nightjar in flight

Plate 42. (Left). Tawny owl

Plate 43. (Right). Whinchat

Plate 44. (Left). Turtle dove and young

Plate 45. (Right). Garden warbler feeding nestlings

Plate 46. Adder or viper, Britain's only poisonous snake

Plate 47. Weasel with its prey—a field vole

Norfolk marshes have been partly drained to give valuable grazing. In the Wash these muds are termed Fen Silt, the reclamation of which has been mentioned above.

On the blown sand and, to a lesser extent, the gravel deposits, are to be seen the earliest stages of colonization by vegetation and the formation of raw sand and gravel soils.

Alluvium

Apart from Fenland and Broadland, alluvium occurs in all the major valleys of the area, sometimes associated with minor areas of peat. On it are formed immature alluvial soils and ground-water gleys (see Plate 18).

THE FOREST AREAS

Lynn Forest

The Lynn Forest is rather heterogeneous. Its western parts are planted on mainly podzolic soils on the Cretaceous sands, and similar soils also occur east of Grimston on outwash. Near Hillington there is a block on slightly gleyed soils on drift over Gault. Round Weasenham and Rudham the plantations are on brown earths formed from decalcified drift over the Chalk.

Thetford Forest

The two north-westerly portions of Thetford Forest, around Swaffham, lie on podzolized soils on the Cretaceous sands and on gleyed soils derived from drift over Gault. The rest of Thetford Forest is in the Breckland, on drifts of varying thickness over chalk. Locally these drifts are very sandy. There is a considerable range of soil types in this area from rendzinas to deep podzols together with raw sand soils and gleyed soils in valleys. It is probable that future work will show significant differences in tree growth on these different soils: it is already evident that there is a correlation between depth to the surface of chalky substrata and attacks by the harmful root fungus *Fomes annosus*.

Walden and Lavenham Forests

The woods in these two areas, one near Saffron Walden and the other close to Lavenham, lie mainly on heavy-textured more or less gleyed soils on deep till which covers the Chalk to a considerable depth.

Wensum Forest

The Wensum area is again a very heterogeneous one. To the north-west the woods are on brown earths derived from Gipping

Till or its outwash, to the north on mainly podzolic soils on the outwash deposits of the Cromer ridge, and to the south-east on brown earths chiefly formed from Norwich Brickearth. In the last-named area there are locally some podzolic soils derived from outwash.

GEOLOGICAL FORMATIONS PRESENT IN EAST ANGLIA

(Certain minor formations which are unimportant for the present purposes are included for completeness but are not described in the text)

QUATERNARY	(HOLOCENE OR RECENT)	Post glacial	DRIFT FORMATIONS Shingle, blown sand, alluvium Fenland and Broadland Deposits
	PLEISTOCENE	Hunstanton Glaciation	Hunstanton Till and outwash
		Ipswichian Inter-glacial	Morston raised beach, Lacustrine deposits
		Gipping Glaciation	Gipping Till and Outwash
		Hoxnian Inter-glacial	Nar Valley Clay, Lacustrine Deposits
		Lowestoft Glaciation	{ Lowestoft Till and outwash Corton Beds Cromer Till and Norwich Brickearth
		Cromerian Inter-glacial	SOLID FORMATIONS *Leda myalis* Bed { Arctic Freshwater Bed Cromer Forest Bed Weybourne Crag, Westleton Beds (?) Chillesford Beds Norwich Crag Red Crag
TERTIARY	PLIOCENE		Coralline Crag
	EOCENE		London Clay Reading Beds Thanet Beds
MESOZOIC	CRETACEOUS	Upper	Chalk Upper Middle Middle Lower Gault, Hunstanton Red Rock
		Lower	Carrstone Snettisham Clay Sandringham Sands
	JURASSIC	Upper	Kimmeridge Clay

Aldewood Forest

This forest includes large areas of the Suffolk heaths. The plantations are almost entirely on light-textured podzolic soils or acid brown earths formed from the glacial sands and gravels with minor areas on the Crags and Westleton Beds.

To the north, two outlying westerly blocks, near Brooke, are planted on gleyed soils on the moderately heavy-textured till of south-east Norfolk. East of them, near Fritton, is a large plantation on podzolic soils derived from outwash.

BIBLIOGRAPHY

Chatwin, C. P. (1954). *British Regional Geology. East Anglia and adjoining Areas.* HMSO.

Briers, F. (Editor) (1961). *Norwich and its Region. Brit. Assn.* See especially: *Geology:* G. P. Larwood and B. M. Funnell. *Physiography:* J. A. Steers. *Soils:* R. M. S. Perrin. *Chief Norfolk Habitats:* J. M. Lambert.

Hey, R. W. and Perrin, R. M. S. (1960). *The Geology and Soils of Cambridgeshire.* Camb. Nat. Hist. Soc.

Larwood, G. P. and Funnell, B. M. (Eds.) (1961). *The Geology of Norfolk.* Trans. Norfolk and Norwich Nat. Soc. *19*, Pt. 6.

Roxby, P. M. (1930). *Essays in Regional Geography VIII East Anglia.* Cambridge.

Steers, J. A. (1942). The Physiography of East Anglia. *Trans. Norfolk and Norwich Nat. Soc.*

APPENDIX

SOIL TYPES FOUND IN EAST ANGLIA

This appendix is intended to give brief definitions and descriptions for those readers who are unfamiliar with pedological terms. The soils are described only in the forms in which they occur in East Anglia.

PODZOLS

These are moderately to strongly acid soils in which downward translocation of humus and, to a lesser extent, iron has taken place. There is generally a mat of poorly decomposed raw humus which overlies a purplish grey leached or *A horizon*. The B_1 *horizon* (humus accumulation) is very dark brown and the B_2 (iron oxide accumulation) a reddish-brown; but these two horizons are often merged, especially in the Breckland, into a coffee or chocolate-brown horizon, slightly darker at the top and redder at the base. The *C horizon* or parent material is usually a yellowish sand or gravel. These soils probably originally formed under heathland following clearance of scrub oak by early man.

Gley podzols are similar soils but in addition there is gleying and/ or rusty mottling due to the presence of ground-water (see below).

BROWN EARTHS

These are slightly acid soils in which a dark grey-brown *A horizon* merges gradually downwards into a yellowish-brown (*B*) (pron. 'B-bracket') *horizon* of strongly weathered material. This in turn merges into the *C horizon*, although there may be little perceptible difference in strongly weathered drifts. These soils probably formed originally under deciduous forest but in most cases they have been modified by long cultivation.

On light-textured parent materials the soils are of a lower base status, more acid and incipient podzolization is shown by a slight bleaching of the *A horizon* (*podzolic brown earths*), or movement of fine clay may have produced a *textural B horizon*. In low sites or on heavier parent materials there may be some gleying and/or rusty mottling at depth (*brown earths with gleying*).

Brown warp soils are superficially similar to cultivated brown earths, or brown earths with gleying, but have been formed by the reclamation of marsh gleys.

GLEY SOILS

In gley soils, exclusion of air by excess water has led to the chemical reduction of iron with consequent bleaching or *gleying*. Locally in the profile slightly better aeration has allowed re-oxidation to take place to give concretions or mottles of reddish-brown iron oxide. Gleying and rusty mottling may be seen separately or together. The excess moisture may be due to a high ground-water level in permeable deposits (*ground-water gleys*) or to impermeability of the parent material (*surface-water gleys*). The reaction of these soils ranges from slightly alkaline to moderately acid according to the nature of the parent material and/or ground-water.

In extreme cases oxidation of organic matter is inhibited and a peaty surface develops (*peaty gleys*). *Marsh gleys* are a special form formed under salt marsh on the coast. Apart from the presence of soluble salts, they are characterised by a fairly high pH and an inky-black gley horizon containing abundant ferrous sulphide.

CALCAREOUS SOILS

Rendzinas have shallow grey or nearly black calcareous *A horizons* which overlie highly calcareous parent materials. With progressive leaching they develop into *brown calcareous soils* which are similar in appearance to brown earths but contain varying amounts of free carbonate.

ORGANIC SOILS

Organic soils are derived mainly from the partly decomposed remains of vegetation. In East Anglia they are virtually all *basin peats* derived from reedswamp and carr vegetation with some admixture of alluvium. The peat is usually very dark brown or black and the profile reflects episodes of deposition rather than pedogenic processes.

IMMATURE SOILS

These soils consist of little-altered parent material with slight darkening by organic matter. The profile is shallow either due to recent deposition of the parent material or to erosion. The main varieties in East Anglia are *immature calcareous soils, immature alluvial soils* and *raw sand and gravel soils.*

Lodge House, near Stratton Strawless

ANTIQUITIES AND HISTORY

BY R. RAINBIRD CLARKE

By Rome's dim relics there walks a man
Eyes bent; and he carries a basket and spade
Can I guess what impels him to scrape and scan?
Yea, his dreams of that Empire long decayed

Thomas Hardy: *The Roman Gravemounds*

MOST OF the land selected for afforestation in East Anglia since 1920 is marginal from the viewpoint of the modern agriculturalist. But these lighter soils, mainly of sand with only a small admixture of clay, are just those which most attracted the earliest farmers. These soils were easy to till with the primitive equipment available, and the light natural woodland they supported could be cleared by these pioneer farmers who were unable to exploit the more densely forested heavy soils of central East Anglia until Roman and later times. The modern forests coincide, therefore, with many of the areas selected for settlement by Neolithic and later prehistoric farmers, and some of the surviving ancient monuments in the East Anglian forests are connected with the activities of these earlier settlers.

The heavier soils of central East Anglia separate two extensive areas of lighter soils which were the most important centres of early settlement. On the west lies the Breckland zone which embraces not only the Breckland of north-west Suffolk and south-west Norfolk but also the Greensand Belt further north, and includes the modern woodlands of Thetford Forest and Lynn Forest. Between central Suffolk and the coast lies the Ipswich zone, a sub-region known to geographers as the Sandlings. This includes the modern forest of Aldewood with the Waveney Woods in Lothingland as a northern outlier. There was also prehistoric occupation on the sand and gravel terrain of the Cromer-Holt ridge in north Norfolk and on the heathlands which lie some ten miles north of Norwich. On the modern forestry map these further areas of early settlement are represented by the woodlands and scattered plantations around Aylsham, known collectively as Wensum Forest.

Here an attempt is made to summarize the principal trends in the human history of the areas now controlled by the Forestry Commission, and to draw attention to the more important visible monuments in and adjacent to the new forests. It must, however, be realized that it is impossible to dissociate the story of the forested areas from their wider background.

THE HUNTERS

No structures earlier than the Neolithic Age can be seen in East Anglia, but groups of hunters had dwelt in the area intermittently for nearly half a million years before the first farmers reached our shores. Their presence is proven by their discarded flint tools, frequently incorporated in sands, gravels and clays deposited or rearranged by the ice sheets which invaded the area between its periods of human occupation. These Palaeolithic hunters made hand-axes and other flint tools at the temporary camping sites established while they were engaged in the pursuit of game. The area now occupied by Thetford Chase was a favoured hunting ground during this long period, and numerous sites utilized by Palaeolithic hunters can be traced along the valley of the Little Ouse between Thetford and Brandon, and also amid the modern plantations at Elveden and at High Lodge, Mildenhall. Similar tools have also been discovered further north in the gravels of the Cromer-Holt ridge showing that this area too was visited by the wandering hunters.

After the waning of the Last Glaciation a series of climatic and vegetational changes took place in East Anglia and the first period of this Post-Glacial era is known as the Mesolithic Age. During part of it the average summer temperature was several degrees higher than it is in this area today. The melting of the great ice-sheets led to a rise in sea-level, and by about 5000 B.C. the low-lying fen linking East Anglia to the continent had been flooded, thus

63

making Britain an island. Throughout this Mesolithic Age, from about 8000 to 3500 B.C., hunters roamed over this area and their equipment, of which only the flint component normally survives, reflects the varied environments favoured by separate cultural groups. The equipment of one group is characterized by axes suitable for felling woodland and this is well represented at Two Mile Bottom, Thetford. At Wangford in north-west Suffolk, only a few miles away, a temporary camping site of another group of these hunters and fishers has been found on the sand-dunes bordering the fen. Here the surviving equipment is characterized by microliths—minute flints of geometric shape. There is an absence of heavy cutting tools like axes, suggesting that the members of this culture lived mainly in treeless localities.

THE FIRST FARMERS

The warmer and wetter conditions which prevailed during the latter part of the Mesolithic Age stimulated the spread of mixed-oak woodland and the presence of this in Breckland is proven by an examination of pollen grains preserved in the muds deposited on the bed of the former Hockham Mere. Red and roe deer, the formidable aurochs and the wild boar, as well as many smaller animals, roamed the Breckland woods when the first Neolithic farmers arrived about 3500 B.C. Some may have come from the Low Countries and others from southern England to settle in Breckland and west Norfolk.

Here their womenfolk tilled the lighter soils, cultivating the grain plots with hoes. Rapid exhaustion of the soil led these peasant cultivators to move their settlements from time to time, and a gradual increase in population led to an expansion of the cultivated area. Some of this land was gained by clearance of woodland by the slash-and-burn technique. After a few crops had been grown the plots were abandoned and grazing stock subsequently prevented the regeneration of woodland, so that the Breckland heaths gradually expanded.

The felling of woodland required a plentiful supply of axes, and some of these were imported from, for example, the Lake District, Teesdale and Cornwall, but the majority were made from the good quality black flint present in the local chalk. This was chiefly exploited by open-cast mining or by sinking deeper shafts with lateral galleries. The principal mining site in Breckland, and the best known site of this type in Britain, is called Grime's Graves, now in the custody of the Department of the Environment (Plate 24). It occupies a stretch of heathland in the parish of Weeting and is almost surrounded by Forestry Commission woodland. Here the

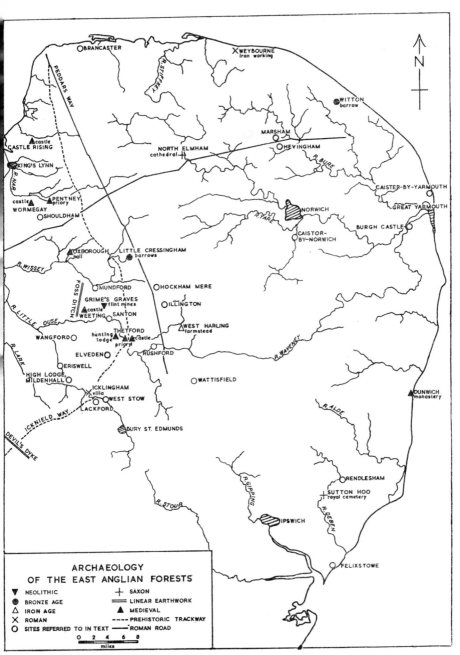

ARCHAEOLOGY
OF THE EAST ANGLIAN FORESTS

▼ NEOLITHIC   ✛ SAXON
⊛ BRONZE AGE   ═ LINEAR EARTHWORK
△ IRON AGE   ▲ MEDIEVAL
✕ ROMAN   - - - PREHISTORIC TRACKWAY
○ SITES REFERRED TO IN TEXT   ── ROMAN ROAD

0 2 4 6 8
miles

Archaeological map

5A

sites of nearly 400 mines can be seen, each marked by a shallow depression surrounded by the grass-grown tips of chalk and sand extracted from it by the Neolithic miners in their search for the best quality flint—the 'floorstone'. The flint nodules were trimmed into the shape of axes at numerous sites around the mines, while the final grinding and sharpening were probably carried out by the actual user of the tool. Visitors to Grime's Graves can descend one of the deeper mine shafts which have been re-excavated during this century where they can see the entrance to the low galleries along which the miners crawled to extract the flint about 4,000 years ago. It is hoped that another mine, now being re-excavated, will also be opened to the public. (See Plates 24 and 59.)

In addition to the immigrant Neolithic farmers and miners whose presence in Breckland and elsewhere on the lighter soils of East Anglia is indicated by characteristic pottery, flint tools, burial mounds and mines, there were other groups of Mesolithic stock who had assimilated some of the new ideas of the first farming communities. These again are well represented in Breckland and also in north-east Norfolk near Aylsham. During the latter part of the Neolithic, East Anglia received fresh groups of people from Holland and the Middle Rhine—the Bell-Beaker folk. These people were nomadic pastoralists who supplemented the products of their herds by fishing and fowling. Their temporary encampments are revealed by fragments of their characteristic pottery, flint tools and bones of their domestic animals, and these sites, together with the round barrows which covered the remains of their chieftains, show that these people roamed the heaths of Breckland, the Cromer-Holt ridge and the Sandlings area of south-east Suffolk near the Deben estuary.

Another Late Neolithic group which take their name from their characteristic pots are the Necked Beaker people, and this culture persisted into the Early Bronze Age. These nomadic herdsmen lived mainly on the Breckland heaths, on the Cromer-Holt ridge and on the heaths of south-east Suffolk, but in the latter area in smaller numbers than the Bell Beaker folk from whom they are partly derived. Broken pottery, flint tools and hearths remain at the sites of the temporary camps of these herdsmen, but the only visible monuments are the round barrows covering the inhumed remains of their distinguished dead. Hearths, probably made by pastoralists of this culture, have been found during forestry operations on Edgefield Heath on the Cromer-Holt ridge.

From Neolithic times onwards there was constant movement along the chalk ridge running through north-west Suffolk and west Norfolk. A series of trackways, later known as the Icknield

Way (see map) indicate this important route from Wessex, which can be traced through the Thetford Forest on its way north to reach the coast at Hunstanton.

During the ensuing period, the Bronze Age, which lasted from about 1800 to 500 B.C., the bulk of the population of East Anglia were pastoralists though towards the end of the period some permanent farms were established in parts of the area. Later plough-ing has destroyed all traces above ground of farmhouses and fields of this, as of subsequent, prehistoric periods, and the only visible monuments of the period in East Anglia are round barrows. Many of the surviving examples are in or adjacent to Forestry Commission woodlands which have often been planted on heathlands where barrows have escaped the destructive levelling action of the plough. Many occur in Thetford Forest, on the Cromer-Holt ridge and in Aldewood Forest while others are scattered over west Norfolk and the heaths lying to the north of Norwich. Antiquarians and treasure-hunters in the past have mutilated many of these mounds, leaving few for modern excavators to examine. One of the very few which has been excavated adequately lies in Witton Wood in Wensum Forest. This mound was erected over an inhumation burial in the Early Bronze Age, and subsequently enlarged when a fresh ditch was dug round it and a number of cinerary urns containing cremations inserted. In some of the Breckland meres remains of pile dwellings were found in the last century but are no longer visible. These structures were probably occupied during part of the Late Bronze Age when the water-level in the meres was lower than it is now.

THE IRON AGE

The earliest settlement of this period in East Anglia, and probably one of the earliest in the country, began about 550–500 B.C. This is the farmstead site at West Harling, where two timber-framed round houses for the farmer and his stock have been excavated on Mickle-moor Hill near the River Thet. Here the peasant farmers cultivated cereals, grazed their sheep and cattle and hunted wild animals and birds. This farmstead is dated by the fragments of domestic pottery thrown into the shallow drainage ditches round the houses, which now lie beneath the plantations of the Forestry Commission.

About the middle of the third century B.C. the peasant population of the Breckland zone was overrun by a warrior aristocracy of French origin. These immigrants and their new subjects formed the tribe known subsequently as the Iceni, who held sway over all Norfolk and north-west Suffolk, south-eastern Suffolk lay within the orbit of another tribe, the Trinovantes. The skeleton of one of these Icenian chieftains of the late third century B.C. was found with his sword at Shouldham, close to Lynn Forest in west Norfolk.

During the early part of the first century A.D., part of East Anglia was invaded by the Belgic tribe of the Catuvellauni, who had arrived in south-eastern England about a century before. After annexing southern Cambridgeshire, they spread north-east along the chalk ridge into north-west Suffolk and overran the Iceni in that area. The outworks of Thetford Castle may date from this period, when the Iceni in Breckland were hard pressed. But for the respite of the Roman invasion in A.D. 43, the Iceni would probably have been entirely subjugated, as their neighbours to the south, the Trinovantes, had already been.

THE ROMAN AGE

The territory occupied by the Catuvellauni, which now included south-east Suffolk, was at once annexed by the Romans, but the realm of the Iceni survived as a client kingdom for nearly twenty years, despite an abortive revolt in A.D. 47–8. Their independence finally came to an end after the failure of the large-scale rebellion of Boudicca (Boadicea) in A.D. 60–1, when the power of the Roman conquerors was severely shaken. The punitive measures taken after its defeat included the destruction of farms and cottages and the deportation of some of the survivors. For nearly two generations, the process of Romanization in East Anglia was slower than elsewhere, but had become normal by the early second century. The construction of long straight roads was one of the earliest features of this imposition of Roman ways of life on the native population. Some of these cut through the thick forested areas of central Norfolk and Suffolk, while the Peddars Way (see map) followed the line of the west Norfolk ridge northwards from Stanton in Suffolk. This road may still be traced through much of Thetford Forest, and there was an important settlement where it crossed the River Thet at the junction of West Harling and Brettenham parishes. The *agger* of another Roman road, which crossed Norfolk from east to west and eventually traversed the Fens, may be seen amid the plantations on Marsham Heath in Wensum Forest.

As in prehistoric times, the lighter soils of East Anglia were intensively cultivated during the Roman period, but the distribution of farmhouses shows that some of the mixed-oak forest in the central part of the area was felled for conversion to farmland. Few, however, of the villas or big farming estates coincide with the modern forestry areas, though there is a small farmhouse of this period at Icklingham near the south end of Thetford Forest. The Breckland heaths at this time probably supported large numbers of sheep, for there are indications of domestic woollen industry in this region. On parts of the Cromer-Holt ridge the modern plantations cover hundreds of infilled shafts dug to extract low-grade iron ore, some probably, though not certainly, in the Roman period. The juxtaposition of suitable clay for potting and supplies of brushwood for fuel led to the building of kilns for the manufacture of domestic crockery. Though many isolated pottery kilns have been found scattered over East Anglia, indications of pottery production on a larger scale have been discovered at Hevingham and Brampton near Wensum Forest and at Wattisfield in north Suffolk.

The administrative centre of Roman East Anglia was at the small walled town of Caistor-by-Norwich, which is far from the modern forests, as was the port at Caister-by-Yarmouth, developed for trade with the Rhineland. The most spectacular site of the later Roman period in the area is the coastal fortress at Burgh Castle, not far from the Waveney woods of Aldewood Forest. Its function was to guard the estuary of the Yare, Bure and Waveney from the raids of Anglo-Saxon pirates. Other similar fortresses belonging to the series erected along the south-east coast from the Wash to the Solent included those at Brancaster and at Felixstowe. Effective Roman control broke down during the first two decades of the fifth century, and, with the withdrawal of the last Roman troops, the province lay open to raiders and gradually lapsed into barbarism.

THE EARLY SAXON AGE

It now seems likely that the first considerable movement of Anglo-Saxon settlers into eastern England took place between 400 and 425 before the end of Roman control. These barbarians were brought in as mercenaries to strengthen the defence of the area against their own compatriots and other invaders. During the fifth century other Anglo-Saxons arrived from north-west Germany and Denmark. Excavations at West Stow have uncovered the remains of the small huts, timber halls and weaving sheds of a village which probably began as a mercenary settlement soon after 400 and ended about 650–700. The presence of farms and villages can be inferred from the discovery of graveyards; in some the cremated remains of the dead were placed in urns, as in the cemeteries found at Illington, Rushford and Lackford in Breckland, while in others, as at West Stow, Eriswell and Mundford in the same area, the burial rite was inhumation. Almost the only surviving monuments of this period in East Anglia are the linear earthworks, or long banks and ditches, which were built to impede progress along important routes. The most spectacular example is the Devil's Dyke, which bars the line of the Icknield Way across Newmarket Heath, while a slighter example of the same type, the Fossditch, can be seen in Thetford Forest running for 5½ miles between the natural obstacles of the Wissey and Little Ouse valleys.

By the middle of the sixth century, Norfolk and Suffolk and some of the territory to the west had been welded by the Wuffing dynasty into the kingdom of East Anglia. The political nucleus of this realm lay in south-east Suffolk, where invaders from Denmark, under a royal family of Scandinavian origin, established their power in the early sixth century. The royal seat was at Rendlesham near Aldewood forest, and the royal cemetery lay close by at Sutton Hoo, where at least ten barrows mark the resting places of its monarchs. One of these barrows, excavated in 1939, was a cenotaph for an East Anglian king who must have died between about 630 and 670, for the mound covered the remains of a sea-going ship in which had been placed an incredible collection of royal treasures. This remarkable find has been described as 'the most significant, as it is certainly the most spendid, archaeological discovery ever made in the British Isles'. The regal character of this burial without a body is shown by the presence of a giant sceptre, as well as by the immense wealth represented by the gold objects and other treasures.

It was during the early seventh century that the pagan Anglo-Saxons in East Anglia became converted to Christianity, and the seat of the first bishopric was probably established at Dunwich on the Suffolk coast, though coastal erosion there has probably removed all traces of any buildings of this period. Within a few years it was recognized that East Anglia was too large an area to be administered ecclesiastically from such a peripheral site. The diocese was accordingly divided, and a separate see was established for Norfolk at North Elmham.

LATE SAXON AGE

This period of two centuries from 850 to 1066 coincided with the Danish conquest of eastern England. This began as a series of piratical raids, developing into a large-scale invasion in 865. Four years later, the invaders established their winter quarters at Thetford, an important village where the Icknield Way crosses the Little Ouse and Thet, and their forces ravaged the surrounding countryside. After the defeat of the Danes in 878 by Alfred of Wessex, part of the Danish army settled in East Anglia, and their settlements are indicated by the place-name terminations— *by, thorpe, toft,* and *thwaite,* or by Scandinavian personal names.

Santon Downham Church, near Brandon

Most of these names occur in the eastern parts of Norfolk and Suffolk, and only a few are recorded from the modern afforested areas. A Danish burial with an iron sword and two tortoise brooches of the late ninth or early tenth centuries has been found at Santon in Thetford Forest, but the archaeological evidence for this widespread warfare is scanty. Much of our information about events in southern England at this time comes from the Anglo-Saxon Chronicle kept by various monasteries. By 920 the Anglo-Saxon kingdom of England had reconquered East Anglia, but in the late tenth century Danish raids began again and, in the following century there were further large-scale attacks in which Thetford was burnt by the invaders in 1004 and again in 1010. The latter disaster took place after the Danish victory at 'Hringmara Heath,' a locality which may be identified either with Ringmere in East Wretham or with Rymer south of Thetford. For about a generation after this, East Anglia, in common with the rest of England, was under Danish rule.

Warfare looms large in the surviving historical records of this period, but despite widespread devastation there was considerable economic advance in East Anglia during the Late Saxon Age. Even before the close of the Early Saxon Age in the ninth century, trading centres had begun to develop at Ipswich, and probably at Norwich, under the stimulus of commercial contact with the Rhineland. By the eve of the Norman Conquest at least eight towns can be recognized in East Anglia, of which the largest, with populations of up to 5,000 were Norwich and Thetford, followed by Dunwich and Bury St. Edmunds. Excavations at Thetford in recent years has revealed something of the plan and structures of a Late Saxon town, and has shown that its real expansion from a village to a town of considerable importance took place after the Danish settlement at the end of the ninth century. Thetford was an administrative centre with a mint, and some of its inhabitants were engaged in farming and industrial activities such as metal-working, pottery making and woollen manufacture. The religious centre at North Elmham, however, never developed into more than a village, and only the ruins of its cathedral testify to its former ecclesiastical importance.

The growth of the towns was partly due to the expansion of population in the countryside during this period. Extensive deforestation took place to enlarge the area available for cultivation, and to provide space for new villages and farms. By 1066 East Anglia had a minimum population of 60,000, and the true figure is probably four or five times greater, thus making it the most densely populated region in Britain at this time.

THE MIDDLE AGES

Medieval East Anglia was a region of great wealth, created by a dense population supported by an efficient system of agriculture and by extensive industrial activities. The expansion of population noted in the Late Saxon Age continued until the thirteenth century, with the establishment of fresh villages and hamlets on land reclaimed from the remaining forest and heath. During the Later Middle Ages there was a retreat from the less productive soils, especially in west and north Norfolk, and, by the end of the fifteenth century, over forty villages had been abandoned or reduced to a church, a farmhouse and a few cottages. These abandoned or diminished villages are common in Thetford Forest and include such places as Buckenham Tofts, Colveston, Little Hockham, Keburn, Lynford and Sturston. Over the lighter soils of west and north Norfolk the 'foldcourse' system of husbandry prevailed in Medieval times. Within the bounds of a foldcourse there was a summer pasture for the great flocks of sheep on the heaths and commons, and winter pasture over the fallow portions of the open arable fields. This system led to the intensive dunging of these light soils, and so enabled them to produce heavy cereal crops. Some of the wool from the numerous sheep kept in East Anglia was at first exported, but was later used for the local woollen industry, particularly the making of worsteds.

The important towns of the Late Saxon Age survived into the Middle Ages and were supplemented by a few new towns which grew up round fortresses. Some of these expanded considerably but others remained small. The exploitation of the richer soils of central and eastern Norfolk led to the rapid growth of Norwich which, by the early sixteenth century, was the largest English provincial city. Thetford, on the other hand, was the centre of an area of declining importance and remained economically static. Other towns, like King's Lynn and Yarmouth, which had been small in Saxon times, developed rapidly to become two of the leading ports in the country, while Dunwich was eventually destroyed by the ravages of the sea.

The wealth of these towns and ports is attested by their fortifications, numerous churches and monasteries, and by the rarer merchants' houses. The other chief visible monuments of this period in East Anglia are the village churches, conspicuous for their number and for the magnificence of their architecture. In the less prosperous areas the architectural style of their Norman builders predominates, but where the inhabitants became wealthy in the Later Middle Ages, these modest structures have been replaced by large and richly embellished churches. The wealth of the district is also shown by the number of monasteries which formerly flourished, but the sites of most of these are now heaps of rubble due to the robbing of their extensive buildings for lead, timber and stone in later centuries. Many of these monasteries were concentrated in the towns, especially in Norwich and Thetford, and those in the countryside are usually located on rich farmland. Very few were established on the lighter soils where the modern forests lie, but Bromehill Priory, at Weeting in Thetford Forest, famous for its fair, was one of the few exceptions.

The Norman Conquest led to the erection of a number of feudal fortresses, which controlled important towns and estates. The earliest were motte and bailey castles, of which the Castle Hill at Thetford (see Plate 15) is a notable example, while a variant, the ring-motte, is represented by Red Castle at Thetford. In the twelfth

Oxburgh Hall, near Swaffham

century, timber buildings were replaced by masonry structures, and the finest East Anglian example of a stone keep of this period can be seen at Castle Rising in north-west Norfolk. By Early Medieval times the lighter soils were becoming of secondary importance, and therefore few castles were built in what are now the modern forestry areas. One of the few exceptions is at Weeting where a rectangular moat encompasses the scanty remains of a stone-built castle. Moats are among the commonest surviving monuments of the Middle Ages on the heavy soils of central Norfolk and Suffolk. They were dug round many farmhouses to drain the

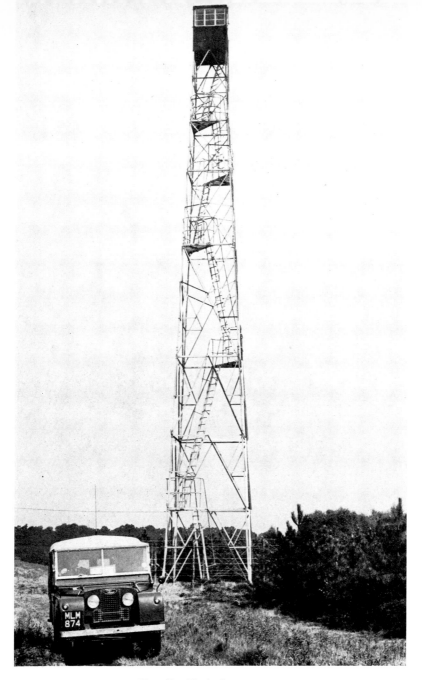

Plate 48.   Fire look-out tower

Plate 49.   Tractor hauling thinnings from a pinewood, using tongs on a hydraulic lift-gear

Plate 50.   A crane loads a bundle of small pine logs at the Brandon depot

Plate 51. Young beech trees planted in drifts through Corsican pine woods

Plate 52. An oakwood underplanted with young beeches

Plate 53. A hydraulic grab loads pulpwood on a forest ride

Plate 54. A flourishing plantation of Hybrid poplars, *Populus* 'Robusta', on the Ryston Hall estate near Downham Market. D4633

Plate 55. Planting Corsican pine on Rendlesham Heath, Aldewood Forest Suffolk in 1921

Plate 56. The same plantation fifteen years later

Plate 57. By 1950, thinning was in full swing; cross cutting logs for pit props

Plate 58. In 1971, after fifty years of tending and thinning, the pinewoods start
to show their mature grandeur

Plate 59. Neolithic miners hacking flints from the chalk of Grime's Graves. A reconstruction in the Castle Museum, Norwich

site though the timber or clay lump buildings have often disappeared in the intervening centuries. A number of moats can be seen in or close to Forestry Commission woods at Brooke, West Harling, Haveringland and Hockham, while at Oxborough near Swaffham a wet moat still surrounds the imposing gatehouse and other apartments of an important late fifteenth century fortified mansion, lineal descendant of the gloomy fortresses of earlier Medieval times.

The Hunting Tower, Gunton Park

Reedbeds at Ranworth Broad

GENERAL INFORMATION

See map on front endpapers.

Thetford Forest. The main centre is *Thetford*, in Norfolk on the A.11 trunk road from London via Newmarket to Norwich. Distances: London 82 miles, Newmarket 20, Norwich 30.

Brandon, Suffolk, another useful centre, lies 7 miles west northwest of Thetford via B.1107. To reach it from London or Newmarket, turn north at Barton Mills roundabout along A.1065.

Santon Downham, the administrative centre for Thetford Forest, lies 2½ miles north-east of Brandon. Take the Thetford road and diverge left after 1 mile.

Alternatively, coming from the Thetford direction along B.1107, diverge *right* 3 miles short of Brandon.

Aldewood Forest. The main blocks, called *Rendlesham* and *Tunstall*, lie east of *Woodbridge*, Suffolk, a town close to the London-Ipswich Lowestoft main road, A.12. Distances: London 80 miles; Ipswich 8, Lowestoft 36. Go north of Woodbridge for 1 mile and diverge east (signposted Orford), following B.1084 to reach Rendlesham. Continue to B.1078 and turn left (north-west) along that road for Tunstall.

The Dunwich block lies near the seaside village of Dunwich, just east of B.1125, which leaves the A.12 at Blythburgh.

Lynn Forest. The main centre is King's Lynn, Norfolk, which is 98 miles north of London A10.

Wensum Forest. This consists of several scattered woodlands around Aylsham, Norfolk, which is 14 miles north of Norwich via B.1149 and B.1145. Distance from London 124 miles.

APPROACHES BY RAIL

All the London services start at Liverpool Street.

Thetford Forest. There are two stations, Brandon, and Thetford, on the line: London–Cambridge–Ely Norwich. Journey time: 2–3 hours.

Aldewood Forest. The nearest station is Woodbridge, on the London–Ipswich–Lowestoft line. Journey time: about $2\frac{1}{4}$ hours.

Lynn Forest. King's Lynn is the terminus of a main line from London. Journey time: about $2\frac{1}{2}$ hours.

Wensum Forest. The nearest stations are Norwich, 13 miles, journey time to London $2\frac{1}{2}$ hours; and North Walsham, 7 miles. North Walsham is on the branch line from Norwich to Sheringham; journey time from London three hours.

BUS SERVICES

These are operated by the Eastern Counties Omnibus Company Ltd., Surrey Street, Norwich, NOR 85B, from whom timetables and details of routes may be obtained.

HOTELS

Leading hotels include:

Thetford: Bell, Anchor.
Brandon: Great Eastern.
Woodbridge: Melton Grange, Seekford Hall, Bull, Crown.
Southwold, near Dunwich: Swan, Crown, Pier Avenue.
King's Lynn: Duke's Head, East Anglian, Globe.

YOUTH HOSTELS

Thetford Forest lies midway between the hostels at Cambridge and Norwich, but is thirty miles from either. Alderwood Forest can be reached from Blaxhall Hostel near Aldeburgh. King's Lynn Hostel is convenient for Lynn Forest. Sheringham Hostel lies close to Wensum Forest.

FACILITIES FOR VISITORS

The following information is drawn from the 1971 edition of

See your Forests. Single copies of this free pamphlet are available from The Forestry Commission, 25 Savile Row, London W1X 2AY. Changes are made from time to time, and the current edition should therefore be consulted for the latest information.

Lynn Forest. Car Park and Forest Trail 1 mile north of Shouldham village at Grid reference TF/677100. Shouldham lies 2 miles east of the King's Lynn–Thetford road, A.134, 10 miles south south-east of King's Lynn.

Thetford Forest. (a) Forest Trail entitled The King's Forest Walk, with *Guide*; 2½p obtainable locally or from Cambridge office (Forestry Commission, Government Buildings, Brooklands Avenue, Cambridge). Starts near West Stow village, just north of Bury St. Edmunds to Mildenhall road, B.1101. From village take by-road north to Forest Office. Grid ref. TL/815715.

(b) Santon Downham Forest Walk (with Guide: 2½p from Commission office nearby) starts at Santon Downham church, on by-road, 2 miles north-east of Brandon, Suffolk. (825870). Includes pinewoods and water meadows beside the Little Ouse.

(c) Six other Forest Walks at suitable points, as marked on Thetford Forest Guide map—see (f) below, also rear endpapers.

(d) Five Picnic Sites with Car Parks:

(1) On Thetford–Mundford road, A.134, 3 miles north-west of Thetford.

(2) On the same road, 6 miles north-west of Thetford.

(3) On Brandon–Mundford road, A.1065, 2 miles north of Brandon.

(4) On Brandon–Bury St. Edmunds road, B.1106, 3 miles south of Elveden Cross-roads.

(5) On Brandon–Newmarket road, A.1065, just north of Mildenhall roundabout.

(e) Arboretum near Lynford Hall, reached from Mundford on A.1065, along by-road (signposted 'No Through Road') that diverges east ½ mile north of Mundford cross-roads. Fine collection of conifers, set in groups.

(f) Thetford Forest Map, 7½p from Cambridge office or local centres, shows situation of all recreational facilities.

(g) Simple camp site at Thorpe Farm, near East Harling. Details in pamphlet: *Forestry Commission Camping and Caravan Sites*, free from F. C., 25 Savile Row, London W1X 2AY.

(h) Camping Sites leased to the Caravan Club at Barton Mills near Mildenhall, Suffolk.

(i) In the Swaffham Section, around 16 miles north north-west of Thetford, Picnic Place and Forest Walk through pine woods on Swaffham–Downham Market road, 3 miles west of Swaffham town, along A.1122, at Grid ref. TF/770090. Camp site on Swaffham–Brandon road, 8 miles south of Swaffham at TL/820970.

Wensum. Car Park and Forest Walk in Bacton Woods, approached down by-road running south from north Walsham–Bacton Road, B.1150, 2½ miles north-east of North Walsham. (Grid ref. TG/317313.) Guide: Bacton Wood Forest Walk, 5p, Cambridge office.

Aldewood Forest, Suffolk. Picnic Site on Woodbridge–Orford road, B.1084, 6 miles east of Woodbridge. Grid ref. TM/355500 in the Rendlesham forest block. Another Picnic Place in the Dunwich forest block, off the secondary road B.1125, 3 miles south south-east of Blythburgh (on A.12 Ipswich–Lowestoft road), in south-east direction towards Dunwich village. (Grid ref. TM/465710.)

Another Picnic Place in the Fritton forest block, 1 mile north of Fritton village, which lies on A.143 Beccles–Great Yarmouth road. Take New Road to Grid ref. TG/465010. Broad views over River Waveney marshes.

MAPS

The whole region is covered by the Ordnance Survey Quarter-inch map, Sheet 14, entitled *East Anglia*.

On the Ordnance Survey one-inch scale, the following sheets of the seventh series are required to cover the forests named:

Thetford Forest, Norfolk and Suffolk	125 Fakenham (for Swaffham blocks only)
	135 Cambridge and Ely (for Methwold and Mildenhall)
	136 Bury St. Edmunds (all main areas)
Aldewood Forest, Suffolk	137 Lowestoft (Dunwich and Waveney blocks)
	150 Ipswich (main blocks called Rendlesham and Tunstall)
Lynn Forest, Norfolk	124 King's Lynn (main areas)
	125 Fakenham (eastern blocks)
Wensum Forest, Norfolk	125 Fakenham (western blocks)
	126 Norwich (main areas)

In Messrs. Bartholomew's half-inch series, four sheets are required to cover East Anglia, namely: 25, Fenland; 26, Norfolk; 20, Cambridge; and 21, Suffolk.

The main regional museum is the Castle Museum in the centre of Norwich. Its many attractions include exceptionally fine panoramas of wild life in Breckland, on the Broads, and along the coast.

The Ancient House Museum in Thetford town has a good collection of more local interest.

MISCELLANEOUS

Water. Ramblers accustomed to upland country should remember that there is no drinkable surface water on these dry brecklands and heaths. You must carry all the liquid refreshment you may need.

Sands. In 1667 John Evelyn, the famous pioneer of forestry in Britain, visited the Thetford district and wrote of:

'The Travelling Sands, about 10 miles wide of Euston (an estate east of Thetford), that have so damaged the country, rouling from place to place, and like the Sands in the Deserts of Lybia, quite overwhelmed some gentlemen's whole estates.'

These are the sands that have now been stabilized and made productive by the modern pine plantations.

Navigation. The Little Ouse was formerly navigable from the sea as far as Thetford. Remains of the curious *stanches*, or lifting water-gates used to control its level in place of locks, may still be seen.

Thetford New Town

Thetford is now a 'new town', or development centre planned to accommodate growing industries and a large incoming population, which include many people from the London area. The old-world charm of its centre has happily been preserved intact. Our aerial photo was taken before the present developments, but, except for a new by-pass road, the scene it presents remains essentially the same.

National Trust Properties

Noteworthy are: Oxburgh Hall, a moated Tudor manor house, illustrated in one of our sketches, which lies seven miles south-west of Swaffham on the south side of the Stoke Ferry road; Ickworth, an eighteenth-century great house in the classical tradition, three miles south-west of Bury St. Edmunds on the west side of A.143; and Blickling Hall, a Jacobean house with a fine landscape park, north-west of Aylesham. The Trust also owns Blakeney Point and Scolt Head on the north Norfolk coast, and Horsey Mere near Winterton-on-Sea, on the eastern side of the county.

Grimes Graves

This famous archaeological site is situated three miles north-east of Brandon to the east of the Mundford road, and can be reached by taking A.1065, then B.1108. It is in the care of the Ancient Monuments Department of the Ministry of the Environment. It is open to the public at reasonable hours at a moderate charge.

Barton Broad at Barton Staithe

Printed in England for Her Majesty's Stationery Office by
Headley Brothers Ltd 109 Kingsway London WC2 and Ashford Kent

Dd.503025. K80. 4/72

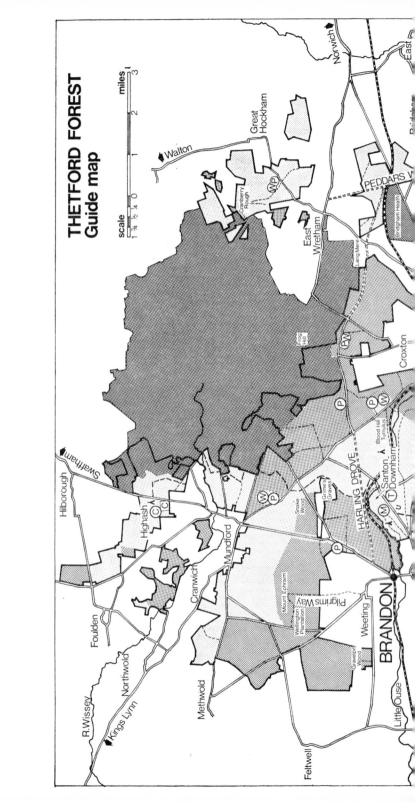

THETFORD FOREST
Guide map

scale
1¾ ½ ¼ 0

miles
0 1 2 3

Norwich

Walton

Great Hockham

Cranberry Rough

WP

East Wretham

PEDDARS W

Bridgham Heath

Lang Mere

Frog Hill

CW

Croxton

P

P W

Blood Hill Tumulus

P

Santon Downham

HARLING DROVE

W

P

Grime's Graves

Snake Wood

M

u

T

Swaffham

Hilborough

Highash

C Y

Mundford

Cranwich

Foulden

Mount Ephraim

Pilgrims Way

Wellington Plantation

Methwold

Weeting

Gravel Pit Wood

BRANDON

R.Wissey

Kings Lynn

Northwold

Feltwell

Little Ouse

East

Bridgham